Diary of a You

Barry Revill

Diary of a Young Boy

Acknowledgements

The author wishes to thank the editors and the following people whose help, tolerance and forbearance have meant this book has finally made it. Each one of you has contributed in your own special way, be it an endless supply of emails, a quiet coffee or two, a suggestion, a thought, or simply to tell me to 'get on with it'. I did!

My thanks are due to the following. To my family.
To Christopher Allen and Kieran Carroll. To my Friday Writing Group.
To Glenda Shepherd, Kathy Smith and Walter McVitty.

Dedicated to Stephen Murray Smith, Ruth Bergner
and Ivan Southall, all of whom helped me with my writing.

Diary of a Young Boy
ISBN 978 1 76109 571 9
Copyright © text Barry Revill 2023

First published 2023 by
GINNINDERRA PRESS
PO Box 3461 Port Adelaide 5015
www.ginninderrapress.com.au

Contents

Balaclava

It was a cold autumn morning and the sun shone lightly on Balaclava Road. I was about four years of age, and it was time to see a bit of the world. Dressed only in my singlet, I left our shop and wandered up to Balaclava Junction. I looked in the shop windows, waved to the lady watering her roses, patted a dog on the nose and had a pee in the gutter. I sat down for a while and watched the trams go by, waved to the conductor and the driver. I was amazed as I watched all the sparks coming off the wheels when the driver applied the brakes.

A lady walked past, then slowly came back to me. 'Ever so dangerous sitting there by the side of the road, ever so,' she said. 'Where do you live, lad?'

I pointed to the shop. She took me by the hand and led me back home. Past the lady watering her roses, past the dog whose nose I had patted and past the spot where I had a pee.

My mum was not impressed. Her face was red, her lips were pressed tight and she was holding a handkerchief in her hand, which I think was wet from crying. 'Where have you been, luv? I've been ever so worried, ever so. I spoke to Fred next door. He spoke to Bert the wood man. Then he spoke to that terrible Mrs Kershaw who's quiet below stairs. I've been out of my mind with worry. I was thinking of closing the shop and calling the police.'

'I went for a little walk and this nice lady found me after I had a pee in the gutter.'

'Went for a walk?'

'Yes, Mum, a walk. I wanted to explore, find things and see things. Like in the book you gave me for Christmas!'

'Well, I never…'

The lady who had found the great explorer was standing by the shop door. She muttered something about having to go now because she had to be home for her Bert.

'Oh dear! I'm terribly sorry. I should have thanked you for bringing my lad home. Ever so kind of you. What's your name?"

'Mrs Tillson. Everyone around here calls me Gert.'

'Well, Mrs Tillson, I would like to thank you for all you've done for my lad this morning. We have some lovely bacon for sale at the moment, only fresh in yesterday. Lovely stuff, middle rashers too! Don't cook it too fast, nice and gentle in the pan, let all the juices do their work! That's what I always say. We have some nice eggs as well, just in from Bayswater. Nice brown ones. Nothing nicer than seeing those lovely eggs popping away next to those lovely strips of bacon. I always give my Les eggs and bacon for breakfast. Hail, rain or shine. Keeps his pepper up. At least that's what he tells me, if you get what I mean, you being married and all that. Now, Gert, I hope you don't mind me calling you Gert, and what would you say to a dozen eggs and all at a reasonable price?'

Outside in the morning, the trams ran past with a rattle and screech. Down by the school gate, the mothers bossed their children into some sort of order, with a kind word here and a box behind the ears there. Kids screamed and yelled, pulled hair, kicked shins, dropped school bags, picked them up, dropped them again and dragged them along the ground towards their class as if they were coming to the end of the world or heading for the cuts.

My mother ran the shop during the day while my father built up a clientele selling butter and eggs going door to door around the suburbs. He was moody. In the evenings, he would sit at the table having a smoke waiting for his meal to be dished. No words, just sitting there, staring.

I had a cocker spaniel called Trixie. It would try to sit by his feet under the table and he would kick it away. After the dog had died, my mother found me early the next morning trying to dig it up from the garden. I was crying my eyes out. In the mornings, I would be found standing by the front gate watching the people walking up and down the street, gazing at the cars going by, admiring the trams, and in wonder at the men marching up and down, left right left, with their eyes to the front. And all the shouting. I thought it all so very strange.

And sometimes, there were little puffs of white clouds high up in the sky and I heard Mum say to Mrs Philips next door that it was from the guns. I had a little chair in the corner of the shop. I would sit there. When people came in, they would ruffle my hair and ask me if I had been a good boy and if I was looking forward to going to school and all that stuff. If I smiled, they gave me a lolly. I tried to smile as much as possible, sitting on my chair in the corner.

After a while, I began to feel like my dog, Trixie, who would sit up on her hind legs for a biscuit. So, when a lady came in one day, I sat up in my chair with my hands in front of me like Trixie and asked her if I could have a biscuit. She told my mum about it and suggested I should be taken to the doctor, or maybe even locked up. Then my mum said if anyone was going to be locked up, it was not me. Maybe the woman in question should be locked up along with her dopey husband, who still owed some money on a bottle of sauce.

Then my mum sort of stared at her and she stared back at my mum, whose lips were all very funny and tight. Then my mum put her hands on her hips, which I had seen her do a couple of times, and she went over to the door of the shop and held it open. She kept staring at the lady, who muttered something about not coming back. My mum said it was the best news she had heard since Pearl Harbor.

Things sort of quietened down for the rest of the afternoon. A man came in and asked if our shop was an ironmonger's. My mum asked him to look at the slabs of bacon hanging up on hooks. He said he would come back later when mum had the nails and screws in, which she promised to get him when she had time to get around to it.

Then a man came in and spoke to my mum about me going to school. I sat quiet in my chair and did not move my hands around like when Trixie wanted a biscuit. He spoke very quietly. He had on a clean white shirt and a big red tie with a lady on it in a bathing suit, which I thought was very rude. He had a little bag with shiny latches on it and he placed it on the floor between his feet. I think he was thinking that I was going to pinch it and run off down the street into the big park, where there were all these trees and big guns pointing out to somewhere. About once a year, men came there early in the morning and stood around, all very quiet as if they were praying. My mum spoke to one very quietly. I did not like it when my mum spoke quietly. It usually meant something was going to happen which I did not like. I watched the man leave. He walked with a sort of limp and as he walked, his bag knocked against the side of his leg because he did not walk straight up and down like other people do. I went to the front gate and watched him walk right up the street to the junction. Then he waited for a while. Soon a tram came along. He hopped on and I never saw him again.

I stood by the front gate for a bit longer. If I sat down low, people could not see me. Sometimes, I could only see their legs, so I knew whether it was a man or a woman.

One day, I saw a couple of nuns and they were all dressed up in this black stuff with beads and things and the wind was catching on their clothes. It made all the beads and things rattle. When they talked, they sort of held their hand in front of their mouths as if they were trying to stop the words from popping out.

But on this windy day, it was the worst. The wind blew down the side of the house and I had to crouch down low to stop being blown away. All that sort of stuff, because it is what can happen on windy days. That is what my mum told me one day. That is what she said then. Anyway, back to the nuns. Real scary. What with the wind blowing, and all the beads and things as well as the mumbling behind the hands and their eyes looking left and right as if they were searching for a boy looking at them from behind the gate. Well, it made me crouch down very low because there is nothing worse than being caught out by a nun.

Mum was in the shop, which was at the front of the house in Balaclava Road. I knew Mum was there because I could hear the wire door being opened all the time as people went in and out. I could watch them too, just like the nuns.

Mum used to put things called curlers into my hair; I think she wanted me to be a girl. Mum used to complain about them getting lost all the time, but I had found a spot down by the back fence where I could throw them over into the lane. There must be thousands of them there by now, all piled up.

Anyway, back to the nuns. I heard one laugh once. Must have been a really funny joke, maybe one of those jokes I'm not supposed to hear. I heard some parts of it when my dad told his mum one day when she was at our place. I think they call them 'dirty jokes'. I will have to find out more about them. Anyway, I heard these nuns laugh, and I ducked down really low on to the ground so they could not see me.

The wind was swishing around all over the place as the tram was going past and the dog across the road was riding on the back of another dog. The nuns were coming down the street with all this swishing sound and all this black clothing stuff. They hid their faces behind their hands. Maybe they had seen or heard something. All I know is that they let out this great giggle which seemed to have gone on for years. Then they walked past. Things quietened down very quickly, and no one went past for a while. I just sat there and thought about things.

I was thinking about my first day at school, which was coming up soon. I would be going with my cousin Ronny, who I think is a bit dumb. He does not know about all the things like I do, and he does not even think about things like I do. He reckons the earth is flat and he told me to just look out my bedroom window one morning to prove it. Well, I did, and I must admit it did look flat, especially down around the clothes line, where there were a couple of tomatoes growing in a little bed up by the fence.

I thought about all that for a while: about things being flat, and some things not being flat, and hills and things, and I wondered about it for a while.

I had been told about going to school, especially the first day. I did not like the sound of it at all. Well, anyway, Ronny turned up for the first day with his mum, Aunty Alma. Mum does not like her all that much. She reckons she drinks. I don't like her much either. When she kisses me, she kisses me on the mouth. It's all sort of sloppy stuff that smells funny. Anyway, Aunty Alma turns up. She is not saying much and Ronny is not saying much either, which for him is pretty normal. So we all stand around a bit, not saying all that much and then it's time to walk over to the school, which is just down the road. Ronny dawdles a bit; he even drags his school bag along the footpath. Aunty Alma clips him over the ears and my mum purses her lips, mumbling something about how mothers treat their kids.

Mum gives me a kiss and a hug at the front gate of the school, where there are all these women crying, which drives me mad. Aunty Alma gives Ronny another clip over the ears again just in case he has forgotten the last one.

It was still cold; in fact, it looked like there was a bit of frost on the flower beds which were on either side of the path that led up to the front door of the school.

We went in and walked down the long corridor. Ronny was moaning about something while still dragging his school bag and wanting to go home. Perhaps he wanted to go up to the bush or down to the beach or play with the girl next door. Anything other than being where he was. I told him to shut up and get on with it, grow up, which did not seem to do anything at all. We came to our classroom, which we had been told about. There were a few kids in there, all in a state of misery and fear bordering on sheer panic. We went in and I found myself a desk right somewhere down the back. Ronny came in and stood just inside the door looking terrible. Then he pooed himself. That was the end of Ronny for the day; in fact, for quite a while.

Raynes Street

We then shifted to Raynes Street. We came into the street on a cold night. My parents found the key to the front door under a brick by the front gate. It was cold and there was little moonlight, so it was hard to see. The house was cold; most of the rooms were without carpets. The kitchen was small with a tiny alcove at one end where there was a sink and a few shelves. Weeks later, my mum found a small trapdoor in the floor of the alcove.

We settled in. My father ran his business from there, selling mainly butter and eggs and general grocery supplies. There was a storeroom at the end of the back veranda where all the supplies were kept, plus a large ice chest out in the garage for supplies, such as the bacon. I reckon I was happy there. As happy as I could be anyway.

There was Val over the road; she had what we called infantile paralysis. There was Lindsay, the kid next door, who, like me, liked getting into mischief. There was Joan over the road. She wanted to show me something in the paddock. She did, and I got the fright of my life, and it took me days to get over it. Mum knew something was up because I heard her say to Auntie Eva, her sister, that there was something wrong with our Barry. He hadn't said a word for about three days. Up in Hawthorn Road there was Mr Shanahan the grocer, the greengrocer, Miss Hewitt the chemist, and, best of all for pies, the Dover Home Bakery. Up by Glenhuntly Road there was the wonderful Camden Theatre for movies on a Saturday afternoon. Life felt settled. I went to Gardenvale Central School and on a scale of one to ten I would have been average.

My father kept a revolver and bullets on the top of a wardrobe in my parents' bedroom. I used to wait until they went out before I would bring it down, load a bullet or two and just muck about. It never went off, but I pulled the trigger a couple of times, taking aim at a lemon on the bloke's tree next door.

I reckon I was happy there. There was a sense of order: kids in the street, shops up the road, a school, movies on a Saturday and there was, of course, the war. Mr Stewart next door, well, he was the local ARP warden. He had a tin hat and a bucket with a little pump thing. He sometimes had a bag of sand as well. I asked him one day how with his bucket and pump thing he was going to stop the Japs when they came round the corner at the bottom of our street. He told me never to mind about that and to go inside or he would thump me behind the ear or worse still give me a kick up the bum. I did not think this was very nice and I told my mum. She called out to Mrs Stewart to come to the side fence, and she told Mrs Stewart what her husband had said to her Barry, who at this stage was hiding behind a bush. Mrs Stewart told my mum to mind her own business. My mum said if she was not careful, she would not be given any more cheap cracked eggs that were rationed because of the war. Mrs Stewart went all red in the face and scratched her nose and jumped higher up on the fence. She said something to my mum about sticking the eggs where the monkey sticks his nuts, which I failed to understand. Then Mrs Stewart stormed down her front drive and pushed the front door shut with a loud bang.

I came out from behind the bush and sort of wandered about a bit. David, my brother, was not doing very much. So I talked him into going into the big ice chest in the garage. I shut the door and then went off to inspect the spiders that I kept in a jar down the side of the house. I was down there for a while looking at the spiders, other things and all the ants walking about the place as if they were in a hurry to go somewhere. Once I got there, it was time to go back again. I must have been there for a while because eventually I could hear yelling coming from the garage. It was then that I remembered David in the ice chest. He was pretty wild and he had gone a funny sort of colour. He reckoned he was going to thump me right and proper when he got bigger. What's more, he was going to tell Mum all about it when she came home from down the shops. I told him that if he did so, I would not pay him back the shilling I owed him. To add to it, I would not give him any more humbugs. He went all quiet when I told him that and he wandered off to do something inside the house.

I walked up the drive to the front gate and stood there watching things. Val, from over the road, waved and I waved back. We kept it going for a while. Then I went over to her place to have a look at her dad's chooks. They were nice chooks: some were pure white, and there were others which were a nice brown colour. I looked at the chooks for a while and then went around to the front of Val's place to have a bit of a talk with her. She was in this long bed thing with big wheels so she could be wheeled around the place a bit. She had these leg irons for when she was out of the bed and she walked with a hell of a limp from side to side, which I reckoned must have been very hard for her.

'Saw you go to the paddock with Joan the other day,' she said.

'I did not,' said I, lying.

'Did she pull her pants down? She does it for all the boys around here.'

'What if she did? It's none of your business anyway.'

'Bet it gave you a fright up there in the long grass with her.'

'Did not worry me at all,' said I, lying some more.

'Anyway, I see lots of things from up here on the veranda. I don't miss much, even people going into the paddock with Miss Hot Pants. Like you, for instance.'

'I'm going now. See you later.'

'OK. Come again soon. I like talking about what you get up to,' said Val with a wide grin.

I had to think of something to do. I loved campfires. I always like them. Liked to see the smoke going up through the trees, watching it curl around and then disappear amongst the leaves. It gave me the sort of peace feeling, as if I was miles from everyone. Way up in the hills somewhere. Sort of over the hill and far, far away. Anyway, on this day my parents were down the street somewhere. My father needed to go to the chemist as his belly was playing up again. He had a 1940s Chev panel van which he used for deliveries. He had emptied it of stock and given it a good clean out for the following Monday morning. It was a cold morning; I think the wind must have been coming off the snow somewhere up in the hills. What better place, I thought, than to light a nice little fire in the back of the van. I got a few dead leaves from under the trees, some tiny bits of timber from the wood heap, some paper and matches from the kitchen and I soon had it all set up to light, just as I had been taught when a cub.

I soon had a little fire going with smoke billowing out at the back of the van. The petrol tank under the car was no concern of mine.

Then Mr Stewart from next door poked his head over the fence. 'What the hell are you doing? Do you want to blow us all up?' he raved. 'First, it's the Japs, now you. What's the world coming to? Get that bloody fire out and get all the ash out and smoke and all that stuff before your parents come home, otherwise they'll have you off to the boys' home.'

I threw the ash and the rest of the stuff behind the garage, cleaned up the floor with some sandpaper and managed to get rid of most of the stain, which I covered with a piece of cloth which I hoped my father would not notice on Monday morning. Then I went up the side of the house to look at my spiders again. After that, I came back and sat on the steps and looked up the backyard and watched a couple of doves preening each other. I watched how they took advantage of the sun and how they always picked a nice sunny spot to sit in.

I felt high and low at times in Raynes Street. Sort of moody. I wondered why my father would not talk to me. I used to watch Mr Hicks over the road talking to his sons Eddy and Les. They would sit on the front steps and talk about things. They would just sit there and talk. I know that's what they did because I used to watch them. I had a special spot on the front veranda behind a big pot plant so I could see all sorts of things, especially when people went past, up and down the street.

Especially when Mr Hicks was talking to his sons. Not sure what they talked about. Maybe grown-ups' stuff. Girls and all that sort of thing. But I used to watch them as they would be sitting, laughing and patting each other on the back. Mr Hicks, well, he would be laughing too. Then Mrs Hicks would come out and I would hear her wanting to know what all the laughing was about. Then they would go all quiet for a while until she went back inside again.

But I used to like watching them laugh. I used to think about it when I was in bed at night. I wondered why my father did not laugh with me or perhaps even put his arm around me and give me a bit of a hug, or maybe even go down to the park and kick a footy. He came into the kitchen the other night just as Mum was setting the table for tea. He muttered something about the day and something about stupid people who have no brains and how they should be shot or put down at birth or something like that. That is what he said. My mum told him to stop it, especially in front of the children. He told her to bag her head. How would she know anyway because she was just a moaning Pom and moaning Poms didn't know anything. That's what he said. Then my mum said she was just as good as he was any day of the week. She was not all screwed up in the head because someone married their first cousin. Then he got this real horrid look on his face and his tongue kept slipping in and out of his mouth, which I did not like. Then he muttered something about wishing he was living up in the bush with his mum, up there at Newstead, not far from Castlemaine.

So I did not like all this. I went off to bed and switched on my bed light and turned on my little Mickey Mouse wireless. I listened to some nice music. Then, from my bookcase, made from a couple of butter boxes, I got out my book, which is called *Along the Track* by Crosbie Morrison. It was where I got all of my information about insects and things, where I learnt things about snake poison, the platypus and also lots of beautiful information about gum trees, which I am very fond of.

Time for sleep now. Tomorrow is another day.

The Bully

He was a big kid, with fat legs that were held tight in his short pants. His eyes were sort of puffed up for reasons that I was never able to understand. But I did not like him and he did not like me. There was a time when we used to talk. I would wave to him when I was down the street and he would wave back. He had a little sister. She had a limp. I saw them by the canal one day and he was hitting her on the face with his fists. I yelled out and told him to stop because I could hear her yelling out and telling him to stop.

He was not in my grade at school, so I did not see much of him. But I used to see him watching me at lunchtime. He always sat on his own over by the peppercorn tree away from all the other kids. Just on his own. I used to reckon he was watching me, that's what I used to reckon about this kid. He would sit there, munching on his lunch, just staring at me, sort of as if he was looking right through me and out the other side. Really scary!

One lunchtime, he told me he was going to get me one day after school. That frightened me. He was such a big kid. Nothing happened for a few days. I thought he might have been joking. But this kid never joked, he never smiled. I always enjoyed my walks home from school. I liked looking into the gardens and seeing what's going on around the place. Looking at the trees, plants and all the pretty flowers, especially when they start to come out in spring.

But one day after school he was waiting for me. Just around the corner from the bottom of our street. He grabbed me. He gouged my eyes, pushed me on to the ground and got himself on top of me and started bashing me around the face. I tried to kick him, but he was too big for me. He twisted my arm until it really hurt.

I screamed out and told him to stop otherwise I would tell my mum. That made it worse, for he twisted it all the more. I thought my arm would break. It happened the next day, and the next, until it reached a point where I had to walk what I reckon was thousands of miles out of my way home from school to avoid him. Then, one day, he gave me a black eye. I showed it to my mum, and she told Mrs Hicks over the road, and she told Mr Hicks when he came home from work all about it. It made Mr Hicks cranky. He told Mrs Hicks to tell my mum he was going to teach me the straight left, which was a boxing punch he knew all about from when he fought at the West Melbourne Stadium.

Mr Hicks was a nice man. He worked in South Melbourne at a timber place and rode his bike each day back and forth, which I reckoned must have been hundreds of miles. He came over to our place one night and told me all about boxing: how to balance on your feet, how to move to miss your opponent's punch, how to conserve your energy and how to wait for just the right moment when you give your opponent the punch that brings stars to his eyes. Mr Hicks also told me all about bullies and how he reckoned they were usually not all that smart and that they usually liked to work in groups. I really liked listening to Mr Hicks. Mum gave him a cup of tea and then Mrs Hicks would come over as well. That meant that Mrs Hicks would then start to tell us all about South Melbourne; the gangs that lived there and all the things that used to go on in the street they lived in. My mum told me later that South Melbourne was a pretty rough area with lots of nasty kids and gangs but not to worry about that because the Hicks family were all okay.

Mrs Hicks liked to have a good talk. One morning when I was leaving for school, she was talking to my mum over the front fence. When I came home from school for lunch, they were still there. I could not understand it and thought about it for hours on end. Anyway, Mr Hicks had given me all the clues I needed to know to beat the bully. I saw him sitting by himself a few times in the schoolyard with a couple of gangs. He was standing on a hill waving his arms around and he looked like he was making a bit of a speech, which seemed a funny thing to do in a schoolyard. That's what I thought anyway.

Then, one day, on my way home from school, he was waiting for me. I came round the corner at the bottom of the hill, past the old gum tree and there he was. He just stood there right in the middle of the path just where I wanted to go. I asked him to please move because I wanted to go home. He just laughed with his stupid sort of giggle that he had. Then he blocked my path and came towards me and grabbed me round the neck and started to grind his fist into my eyes. Soon, he gave me a whopping hit to the stomach followed by an upper cut to my face.

At that moment, I remembered Mr Hicks. The bully came at me again. He swung a wild punch which if it had landed would have finished me. But I ducked and weaved and landed him a heavy punch to the belly. He bent over and I quickly moved in with a mighty uppercut, followed by two perfect straight lefts to his jaw. He had this funny look on his face. Then he came at me again, but I was ready for him. He swung wildly but I was nimble on my feet and his swings went nowhere. Then I hit him again but this time I got in close with a whopping uppercut followed by another, then another. He sank to the ground. I stood back, as Mr Hicks had taught me to do. I kept my fists up and I sure was ready to move on to him again if I felt there was any trouble. He got to his feet. He kept his hands to his side, gave me a nod and walked away.

What is it about bullies? What is it about violent people? I do not understand them; I do not understand why they are so violent. Why are they the way they are? I do not understand this at all.

Tanti Avenue, Mornington

Things started to go wrong in Raynes Street. My parents had arguments. There was talk of my father selling the business. From behind closed doors, I could hear talk about another woman. I did not know who she was or what they were talking about. It went on for weeks. Then things would quieten down a bit and then the rows would start again. I would go to my room and read a book or maybe I would go down the side of the house where I kept my black spiders in an old jam jar.

I am still not clear on exactly how it happened one night when I found myself in an old house in Mornington with a whopping Moreton Bay fig out the front. I have no recall on how we got there but we must have caught a train to Frankston then the bus to Mornington. There was my mum, Aunty Eva, myself and I can recall my sister Beth and my brother David. We had been there about half an hour when the lights fused. Not easy to find a candle in a strange house but we did.

What a strange place it was. I went to sleep in a strange bed, in a strange house and I did not like it. I awoke one night to find my father standing at the end of my bed. He was standing there not saying or doing anything. I did not know what to say. We had been at the house for about a month. I had been going each day on the bus to Frankston High School. He stood there, sort of rocking backwards and forwards on his feet and he had on this big leather coat with a big buckle around the middle of it. He stood looking at me and I lay in the bed looking at him. I began to wonder whether he was a stranger or whether in fact he was my father. He stayed the night. In the morning as I got ready for school, he was gone. I hated the place. Everything I had known had gone. The kids in the street, the shops up the road, the tram at the end of the street and the pictures on a Saturday afternoon: all of this was gone from my life. As far as I was concerned, life was a misery.

On the weekends, I would take off for walks. I would walk around the cliffs down by the beach. There was a bit of a track going up through the scrub along the cliffs, so I would walk along there. I did not know a soul; there was no one to talk to, no one to walk with, so I would just walk on my own until I reached a point where the track cut out and then I would turn round and go back. I would go down to the pier and watch the people fishing. I worked out that fishermen must be the quietest people in the world. I tried to talk to one man and he told me to go away, and I tried to talk to a kid and he poked his tongue out and told me to piss off.

So I would sit on the pier and watch people fish and if they were rude to me, I did not care. My mum had told me not to worry about rude people because most of the time they don't know they are being rude for they do not know any better. So I would watch the waves going in and out and look at the mussels growing under the pier. I would then think about the mussels for a while and how they managed to cling on to the pier with all the waves coming in and out all the time and the storms blowing ever so often, which caused the boats and even some of the bigger ones to be washed up on to the shore.

I went on my walk every weekend and then would go down to the pier.

There was a fish and chips shop in the main street, a dairy, a picture theatre and not much else. I used to stand outside the fish and chips shop and watch the water run down the window on the inside of the glass. I would wave to the man and he would wave back and then he would get on with his job of cooking fish and chips. A lady sat in the corner of the shop with a big pile of potatoes. She had this whopping big knife and she used to sit there peeling the potatoes. I think she must have sat there forever because every time I went past, she was sitting and at work. I used to wave to her and she used to wave back to me. I used to look at all the fish in the window, surrounded by little blocks of ice. I did not like the look of the fish. They did not look all that happy with their eyes staring off into space like that. I think they would have been much happier in the sea.

There was also a library. I joined up and they gave me a nice little card and the lady gave me a long talk about always returning the books on time and how much it would cost if my book was overdue. By the time she had finished, I was beginning to wonder whether to just hand back the card and keep to reading comics. But anyway, I kept my ticket and after ten a.m. on a Saturday I was usually the first there to return a book and borrow another one.

But it was hard. I did not know what to borrow because I did not know what to read. That was the problem. So I would go to the section on early explorers or maybe Australian insects and borrow the books. Then off I would go home with them with the feeling of joy because I had found in reading a feeling of escape. I could indulge myself and for a little time each day, I could be in another world. But at times it was hard to read about something unknown to me compared to a familiar subject. I would read a book and then take it back to the library and tell the lady how much I enjoyed the book. I had thought of telling her how much I enjoyed the index as well but then I thought she would think I was trying to be smart. I always gave her a smile and told her some little bits about the book I liked. I always remembered not to turn down the corners of the page but instead use a bookmark so as not to lose the page I had last read. The library was quiet and this is the way libraries are meant to be. I knew this.

I would then go back home. Mum would want to know where I had been and so I would tell her I had been to the library. It was okay, because she knew I liked it there. The library was down the street not far from the sea and she knew I liked being by the seaside with all its attractions.

I liked special visitors. One special visitor was my Uncle Ted. He had come over to make a new shelf for mum. He had come from Yorkshire in England. I really liked Uncle Ted. He wore a cloth cap, smoked a pipe and when he walked outside the wind would catch the smoke from his pipe and I reckon he looked a bit like Puffing Billy. I believe there is something special about Yorkshire and the people from there. Uncle Ted did not say much. If he was about to say something, whether it be about cricket or how his cabbages were going this year, he would sort of sidle up to the subject having first of all filled his pipe. It was not that he lacked in education or that he lacked in general knowledge. It was simply a matter of him taking his time with his words just like the timber he worked with which he did not like to waste.

So, when he spoke, his words were measured. I reckon he used to speak in centimetres.

'Now, lad, about this shelf for your mum. It has to be done right, you know. Firstly, you need to have good wood or, more correctly, good timber. Then you have to have good tools. Without good tools, all the good timber in the world is a waste of time, and a good tradesman should never waste his time. Do you follow that, lad?'

'Yes, uncle.'

'And the other thing is you have to really think about the job you are going to do and think of how you are going to do it well. That is important otherwise you might go off half-cocked, if you'll excuse the expression.'

'Yes, uncle.'

'The thinking process can be very demanding on the body as well as on the mind. It is therefore very important that you spend as much time thinking about the job as actually doing the job itself. Once the customer understands that when I am sitting in the shade of a tree for a few hours before starting the job, I am actually thinking and planning and applying all of my knowledge and skills towards the preparation of the job in hand. Well, once we understand this thoroughly, we all get along just fabulously.'

'Do you do many jobs, uncle?'

'Funny you should say that, lad. No, not many. But those I do, I do well. And you know, once I've done a good job, well, they ask me back. Then they tell the man over the back fence, and he tells his brother, and he tells some bloke from his work. In that way, one thing just leads to another, so there is always enough for me to do. As there is always enough work, I can put some money aside so that Aunty Eva and I can go back to Yorkshire one day for a visit. That's what I intend to do, lad. I would like to return to Yorkshire for a visit. To see those hills again and those green hills in the morning when the sun starts to creep into the valleys and the soft mist rises up as the morning comes alive. I'll tell you something, lad, you can take your body out of Yorkshire but not your heart and soul. That's a fact, an absolute fact. Sometimes, I wonder why we came out here to Australia. This big brown land of yours. It's so big, and I don't like the heat much in the summertime. Sort of gets to me and it upsets your aunt, my Eva, as well. Makes her feel really poorly some days, not to mention being cranky, but maybe I should not be telling you that. Perhaps it's because this country is so young, maybe that's the problem. I really don't understand, but all I know is that I miss the green of Yorkshire and I suppose I miss England itself.'

'Uncle, when do you think you'll start on the shelf for my mum?'

'Well, lad, that's a very good question.'

He sat back on his chair and filled his pipe, tamping the tobacco down gently as he did so. The smoke drifted up to the ceiling and some of it went out the door and down the hall.

My mum came in. 'Ted,' she said, 'when are you going start on my shelf? You've been sitting here yapping to our Barry for ages.'

'Now, Alice, don't get on so. I've only been sitting here talking to the lad and telling him about Yorkshire. And what's more, I've been telling him all about this job in hand and all the important things that have to be done and which will of course be done by me.'

'Yes, but when?' said Mum, fidgeting with her handkerchief.

'Well, I would say around about what you would call right away. Just as soon as I commence with the measurements, which are most important to a job of this magnitude. You might not think a shelf is very important in the grand scale of things, but a shelf is a shelf, and the job has to be approached with due care and by no means rushed. Any chance of a cup of tea, Alice?'

'Really, Ted, you are the limit. I reckon I could have just about built a house while you've been yapping here to Barry about Yorkshire and all those mists and valleys. You Yorkshire blokes are all the same. In the meantime, could you at least look like you're going through the motions of getting at least some of the job done?'

He sat back in his chair and drew deeply on his pipe. He still had his cap on. In fact, come to think of it, I had never seen him without it, whether it be him watching his pigeons coming into land or whether he was to be found standing quietly in the backyard observing his cauliflowers. Either way, there was something about this man who, I would have to say, was my favourite uncle. I think when I grow up, I will have pigeons because I think there is something restful about them, something sort of peaceful, but I'm not sure whether I can put it into words the right way.

'Tell me, lad, do you ever read?'

'Yes, uncle, I do. I try to read as much as I can.'

He sat back in his chair a bit further but before doing so he had a look down the hall to see whether my mother was on the war path. 'Well, lad, you should read as much as you can, because reading can give you knowledge. But that's where you have to be careful: I've known a lot of people who were supposed to have a lot of knowledge, yet the way they spoke and the way they behaved, well, you would hardly think so, that's for sure. Whatever you read and how much you read, you've got to have time to think about things. That's one reason why I have pigeons. The birds take a bit of time, especially if you go in for races like I do when I turn my mind to it. There's something very special in taking some birds in the basket down to the station, putting them into the guard's van on the train and watching them head off to Shepparton as mine did a few weeks ago.'

'You must really like your birds, uncle."

'Aye, lad, that I do. Just between you and me and the old gatepost, I don't know how I would get on without them. You must not let on to Aunty Eva, or your mum, otherwise I'm going to be in more strife than you can imagine. Aye, that's where it will be. They'll come on to me like a Yorkshire fog as I try to explain to them what the birds mean to a bloke like me and they will not understand. In fact, they cannot understand, it's just beyond their ken. I had seen pigeons flying around and I liked the way some of them did this sort of somersault in the sky.'

'What do you like most about them, uncle?'

He sat lower in the chair and made himself comfortable as if it was going to be some time before he could gather his thoughts. 'Well, it's like this. After you've been feeding the birds for quite a while and cleaning out their pens and making sure all the muck goes onto the vegie garden, well, you sort of get to know them in a friendly sort of way. Maybe I'm not explaining it all that well. I'm not a very educated man, lad. I'm not all that good with words and, as Aunty Eva will tell you, Yorkshire men don't throw too many of them around at the best of times. So I'm doing my best by you, as I hope you can see.'

'Yes, I can see that, uncle.'

I could see clearly that he was thinking really hard about what he was about to say. I could see it was important to him and that he was struggling with the words.

'Well, it's like this. As I mentioned a little while ago, you've taken the basket down to the station and given your birds to the man there. Well, then I go home, and I usually have a cup of tea with your aunt. That's what I always do. Your aunt and I have a bit of a chat and I tell her about how I delivered the birds to the station. Not that she needs to be told, because I've been telling her about it for about three months on and off. Then, one day, when I know it's about time for the birds to arrive, especially my best and keenest bird, well then, it's my time to go and sit outside by the pigeon loft. That is my time, lad.'

'It must be exciting watching the birds come down, uncle.'

'Exciting! That's not the word for it, lad. Not a bit. It's a bit hard for me to explain. I wish I could put words together better, like some folks do. I have all these thoughts about the way I want to describe something, the way I see things, but I just cannot get the words out. Sometimes, I think to myself that it's all a bit unfair, not having an education and all that learning stuff. Any road, that's enough of that. So, I go and sit by the pigeons' loft. It's a nice spot, with a little bit of shade for a hot day. I just sit there. I tell Aunty Eva not to make too much noise, to forget about the washing and watering the pansies.

'Then a funny sort of thing happens. It goes all quiet like. Almost as if there was something up there in the sky controlling things. Quickly, I would look up in the sky and there would be my bird, my champion bird, flying around and catching the sun on its wings, and I would just sit there nice and quiet, and eventually it would come down in a moment or two and it would be all over. I might put my little bird into a race one day but for the moment I'm just as happy sending her off to some place and watching her coming down out of the sky for me again. It's such a grand sight watching them fly, such a grand sight.'

'Here you are, Ted. Here's your cup of tea, before you collapse from overwork,' said Mum, with her teeth clenched and a pretty dark look on her face.

'Now, Alice, there's no need to go on, there's no need to carry on. I've just been explaining a few things to your lad, important things too, I might add.'

'Ever thought of working and talking at the same time? Women do it all the time,' said Mum.

'This is a real nice cup of tea, Alice. I have to say that. A real nice cup of tea. Just as soon as I finish it, me and this lad of yours will be straight away into making this grand shelf of yours. Surely, a grand shelf it will be too, I can tell you.'

'Let's hope I never need a house,' said Mum, as she headed for the door.

It took, on and off, about three days to finish the shelf. I would come home from school and I could see there was progress going on, but Mum was forever in a dark mood about this crazy shelf which seemed be taking forever to be finished. Then it was completed. I came home one afternoon and there were Uncle Ted and Mum standing by the shelf and just looking at it. It looked like a lump of wood on the wall to me. Mum was smiling, which was a real relief.

'That's a grand shelf, Ted, a grand shelf,' said Mum, beaming.

'A cup of tea would be nice, Alice, and would you perhaps have a little bit of cake?'

I went down into the main street one day, where the street ended by the pier. I could see the boats that had come in from the ocean. The clouds hung low over the town that day and the boats were heavy in the water because the catch must have been good out there this time. There were other people on the pier. Some had come to buy fish, and some bargained with the fishermen over the price. There were arguments back and forth, some friendly, some on the darker side as the fishermen tried to explain to someone that there are costs in running a fishing business and times have been tough and so on.

But many of the customers had developed the habit of not hearing one single word of what the fishermen were talking about. They would wait until the fishermen had finished speaking and then they would offer the same price again, sometimes even lower, which added more heat to the arguments, with more noise up and down the pier and with women looking over the side of the pier and peering down into the boats as if they were doing a major inspection of an ocean liner.

So I walked away from the noise and up to the end of the pier and looked down at the waves coming in and out. I used to like sitting there. I could see right out to sea and watch some of the bigger boats coming and going and then I would find myself thinking about my Uncle Ern, who used to camp each summer holidays at McCrae. Another quiet man. We would sit on the beach. He would tell me about the war and his time in the Merchant Navy and how he saw the ships in the distance go down. How he heard the screaming in the distance coming over the water and how sometimes, when they did manage to get any survivors up on to his ship, they were covered in stinking oil. Many of them did not last the night before they died. That was the way it was.

Uncle Ern reckoned he could hear the ships coming up the bay before you could even see them. I tried to listen for them but could not hear a thing. He would then sit there with the sun blazing down and he was never happier than when he was warm and there was sand running between his toes. He had nothing to do all day long but look at the sea and the water. He told me about corvettes, destroyers and minesweepers, how the big ships were there for the protection of the convoys and for them to keep an eye out for U-boats, which was a very important job.

Sometimes when we looked out across the bay, it looked as if you could walk all the way to the other side. It was lovely, calm and flat, with just a few tiny waves coming up on to the shore with a shimmer of the sunlight shining upon the water. There was little traffic on the road at the back of the beach and on the days when the bay was calm, which were most days, there was a peace about the place. There was no thought of the terrible war. But now, though he was quiet, he looked to me as if he was at peace with himself knowing he was lucky to be alive. However, I knew little about all this war stuff. Seems to me that what happens to people when they come back from a war is that they go all quiet. I'm not sure what happens because I have not been told a lot about it. But I know when my mum starts to talk about Uncle Ern on his merchant ship and all the bombing business in London, I know she gets all upset and very annoyed and angry. I find it is a good time to get out of the place and go for a walk down the beach or somewhere.

Tanti Avenue consisted of a few houses and a whopping big place called Sutton Grange. It could still be there. Down by the beach there was this huge Catholic nunnery with a big fence. I would go and stand at the fence and try to work out what on earth was going on in there. I would wave to the nuns and wave again, but they would never wave back to me. I thought that maybe if I threw a brick through their window, well, at least that would start something. That's what I thought anyway. So, having got nowhere with the nuns, I would then start a bit of a walk through the bush on the top of the sea cliffs. My mother told me never to walk through the bush on the sea cliffs because there would probably be undesirable men there. I never saw an undesirable anything there, although I saw a dog once.

I never worked out why my mother kept telling me not to do this or that. It seemed to be a surefire way of getting me to do just that as a matter of course. Never failed. I liked the sea cliffs. There was a seat there high up on the cliffs. I would sometimes take a book there and have a read or maybe I would just sit there and look at the sailing boats leaning over in the water with the wind and all that stuff. I would then see them change course and sometimes they would come close to the shore and I thought they would crash on the rocks or something. Then they would quickly change direction and off they would go again. I used to think how great it would be to have a boat where you could sail off with enough food and drink on board for a week or so. Then just sail off and sail away for a few miles until you came to a little cove where you could drop anchor and just stay there for a few days. I used to think that would be pretty good.

Sometimes there were bigger ships; they were the cargo ships bringing their wares up the bay to Melbourne. Big ships, which often looked as if they were low in the water because of the weight they were carrying, were truly a sight to see. They did not seem to be moving all that much. In fact, they were, because I used to line the front of the ship up with a small branch of a bush and wait to see how long it took the ship to move along the branch. I soon worked out that some ships moved faster than others. That's what I deduced.

Then, one day, I thought I would walk to McCrae. I was not sure how far it was. I thought it might be a few miles. I told Mum that I was going down the street for a while and off I went. I asked a man how far it was. He told me it was about fifteen miles. This really upset me, because I thought it would not have been all that far. So I set off, taking the coast road where I could. If the track left the road and wandered through the bush up on the cliffs, then I took the bush track. There were tall banksias growing with rough branches all sort of twisted and I felt they looked like rough old men. I thought they would look really scary at night. So I kept going because I thought if I could make it to McCrae, there would be some nice people there whom I had met when we went camping there in the summer.

It was hot and I did not carry water. In fact, I did not carry anything at all. After a while, I started to get really thirsty and I did not like it. I did not have a hat, because some kids told me I looked sissy in a hat. So guess what – no hat! It was no fun walking on the road. It was narrow and winding and even though there were few cars, those that did come by rushed past at what I reckon must have been at least a thousand miles an hour. Sometimes, there were kids in the back seats who poked their tongues out as they went rushing past. I did not like that, because I knew that was being rude.

So I just kept walking. The road was hard. Sometimes, the road curved around a bit and I could see down below to the beach where there was clean sand and sparkling water. There were some people down there and I could see kids running in and out of the water. Further to that, I could see where the water was a lighter colour and I knew it meant the water was shallow. Where the water was a dark blue colour, I knew that it was where it was deeper. There were some trees by the side of the road and I knew they were banksias because I had read about them in a nature book and knew all about them. A kid at school told me they were named after the Commonwealth Bank. I knew they were named after Mr Banks who was on the sailing ship with Captain Cook. I thought the kid was a dope, so I thought it best not to tell him.

At times, the road straightened out a bit. When it came to the bottom of a hill and the country had become flat, there were a few shops by the side of the road. The shops would be there for people to buy fish and chips and ice cream or whatever else was available. I would have loved a cool drink or an ice cream but then it would have been nice to have some money as well, which I did not have on me. I walked past the shops, where there were tables outside with paper tablecloths which were flapping in the breeze, and a man came out from one of the shops and looked up and down the street and then picked up a few small rocks from the side of the road and put them on some tables to stop the tablecloths from blowing away.

It was getting hotter and there was hardly any shade on the road. I found a seat and sat there for a while. I could not hear any birds and I knew they always went quiet in the middle of the day, especially when it is very hot. Only dopes like me walk along a hot road in the middle of the day without a hat. A man went past on his bike and I gave him a wave but he just grunted something about kids being nuts to be out in such hot weather and what was the world coming to. Things were not like this when I was a kid, and I heard it all, blowing on the wind as he grunted and peddled his way off down the road, with his socks tucked neatly into his trousers and his hat pulled down firmly on his head.

I was not sure how far I had walked but I was getting tired. I had no one to talk to but I did not mind, because I was used to it. It is what I was used to. There were times when I found myself feeling lonely, as if I wished for some kids next door or over the road but it was not going to happen, and it did not happen. I had to turn back. I was thirsty, tired and I was getting nowhere fast. The sun beat down and the road was hot. I knew I had to turn back.

I turned back and in doing so crossed the road. I found a bush path which led up and away from the road and which curved in amongst some trees. The trees were not tall, and I think they were tea trees but I'm not sure about that. Anyway, they gave me a bit of shade and I started the slow walk back. I came to a small creek which went down a gully and under the road and I could see where it continued and flattened out and finally made its way to the seashore.

I had a drink, which was a great relief. I wondered, now that I was starting to get real hungry, why I had been so dopey as to not bring at least some food with me. Perhaps a banana or maybe an apple? The creek did not look all that good for drinking. I could see houses further up through the bush. The creek was not moving all that much and I could see a couple of tadpoles in the water, which made me wonder a bit. But I drank it anyway. There were grasses growing alongside the creek and I could see where their roots went down into the water. There were a few reeds as well and I could see a few small fish swimming around amongst the reeds and I worked out that fish would have no trouble keeping cool, unlike a dopey kid I know. There were some rocks as well and the fish were darting in and around the rocks and then coming up to the surface to have a look around and maybe catch an insect or two for lunch.

I stayed there for a while and then decided it was time to move on. The sun was still high in the sky and where the track moved away from the trees the ground was hot and dry and was not very firm to walk on. I found my legs were getting tired and I was sweating a lot. I found a couple of other creeks as well, but the water was just as bad. I moved on from them. Some low clouds came in from the sea and blocked out the sun just a little and that was okay by me. Why do I do these stupid things? Why do I always go off on my own? Well, I reckon mainly because there is no one to go with anyway, no doubt about that, that's for sure. But then, when you are on your own, there is no one else to worry about, no one to moan when it gets too hot or cold, and no one to stare off into space, bored out of their brains when you try to point out something in the bush that you reckon is interesting. I think most people do not see a thing when they go into the bush. In fact, I wonder why they go there at all in the first place. Most people seem to have one eye on the door handle of the car as soon as they leave it and when they are told it is time to go home, their faces light up as if they have won a big prize somewhere. That's what I reckon anyway.

I reckon the bush can tell you a lot about people. If you sit quietly in the bush with someone, you can soon tell whether they are taking any notice of the bush around them. And if you try to explain something to them that you have read somewhere, something interesting you have read about gum trees, for instance, you can soon tell whether they are interested or not. They look at the bush, but they do not see it. You have to sit quietly, and this is where I am going to say something real stupid, something kids at school reckon is real dopey. It's like this. If you sit quietly in the bush, and you must sit there quietly for a while, then the bush sort of comes to you, it sort of surrounds you in this sort of envelope of peace and quiet, but I know I am not explaining it all that well, which is why kids reckon I'm dopey. And if you go to a bit of bush that you have not been to for a while, you can see the changes since your last visit. You can see where branches have come down off the trees. You can see where branches have been low on the ground and with the wind you can see little circles on the ground because the wind has made the branches move around and around on the ground causing all this interesting stuff to happen.

But a lot of people do not see any of this. I reckon it's because they don't want to see it in the first place, that's what I reckon. Another funny thing about the bush is when you come to a little track leading off the main track. Sometimes, it is a little animal track, or sometimes it might be where a kangaroo has bounded through the bush, so if you see the odd little branch broken, that can give you a clue. But if it is a bigger track and it looks like it has been used on a regular basis, those are the ones I like to follow. You never can tell where they are going to lead. And when I follow them, I always wonder about the people who might have walked along them. Were they goldminers, or was there a cave hidden somewhere with piles of money just waiting for me to find it?

I followed one once, on the cliffs at Mornington. At first, I did not notice it, but then the wind caught some small branches and they moved away. I could see the beginnings of a narrow track. It looked un-used; there were many leaves on the ground and lots of small sticks. I pushed the bush aside, being careful not to break any of the branches. I followed the track for a little way and after a short while I came to a curve in the track as it dropped down into a little gully. Then there was another smaller track leading up to some rocks and between two of the larger rocks there had been built a small door. I knocked on the door. There was no answer. I knocked again. Still no answer. I gently pushed open the door.

Inside, sitting in a rough-looking chair, was a man. He had on a bowler hat with a large feather sticking out of the top of it. He had on a pair of pink shorts and he wore a jumper which said on the front, 'You can all go to hell'. There was a small table next to his chair and a very untidy-looking bed over in the corner. On the table there were many books and magazines. In the middle of the floor, there was a hole. I could see there had been a small fire there at some stage.

He had a long beard with bits of twigs stuck in it and on one foot he had a sandal and on the other, an army boot. 'What's your name, boy?' he said.

'Barry,' I replied.

'Do you read, boy? Do you learn about things? Do you think about things and try to work out what's going on? Do you do that, boy?'

'Yes, sir, I do. I try to read all the time.'

'Don't call me sir, okay?'

'Okay.'

He shifted in his seat and moved aside the little curtain in front of a tiny window built into the wall. The sun came in and I could get a better look at him. His face had the most horrid scars and he kept moving his hand up to cover it. I looked away but I know he had seen me looking at him.

'Got burnt down a mine years ago. Some of the timber caught fire and the roof came down a bit and I sort of got caught there for a while until they got me out. If you get what I mean. Name's Bob, by the way.'

'Hello, Bob. Pleased to meet you.'

He put out his hand and we shook hands and I thought to myself that it was the first time I had shook hands with a man.

'Would you like a cup of tea and a piece of cake?' he said, with a little grin.

'Thank you, yes. I'm a bit thirsty,' I said.

He lit a small fire in the middle of the floor, starting it off with a few dry twigs he kept in a box in the corner. He kept the fire small but burning fast and it was not long before the billy boiled.

'Hope you don't mind it black. No milk here, I'm afraid.'

'That's okay, Bob.'

He made the tea quickly and he sat there for a while not saying anything. He rocked back and forth in his chair a bit and I kept feeling he wanted to say something, but nothing happened.

Then he said, 'What are you going to do with your life? What are you going to do when you leave school?'

'I don't know. I don't have a clue. Maybe I could help my father in his business, but I don't like the idea of that too much. Then maybe I could do as one of my uncles told me, which is to learn a trade, maybe become a plumber or a bricklayer. Anyway, something, I suppose.'

He passed me a piece of fruit cake. 'Well, I'll tell you what I think. It sounds to me as if you're like a bloke lost in the bush in the scrub somewhere. That's how I see it anyway. You see, it's like this. You either get an education, and the best you can get, or you don't. It's that simple. Now, if you get an education, does that mean that your life will be all roses and peaches and cream forever? Sorry, no, that's not the case either, not for some of the folks I have seen around the place, but that's another story.'

He drank his tea and went quiet again. And as he rocked gently in his chair, I could not quite make out whether he was mumbling or whether he was humming a little tune.

'Everything has a beginning and an end,' he said. 'What goes up must come down. There is a time to love and a time to hate. A time to give, a time to take away. A time to face your enemy and a time to turn the other cheek. Now, where was I? Ah yes, now, your education. Well, I've told you what to do. It's up to you to do it. But, above all else, you must read. You must read everything and anything you can get your hands on. There's a reason for that, because when you read, and you think about what you're reading, it gives you something to think about. And I will tell you another thing. I think there's a difference between the people who read and the people who don't. That's what I think, anyway.'

'But Bob, how do I know what to read? How do I know where to start?'

'Well, lad, that's not an easy question to answer, and I don't want to send you down the wrong track. Firstly, you join a library. There are good ones and bad ones. You need to have a library where the staff will not look down on you as a kid but will give you all the encouragement in the world. That's important, and anyway, in an ideal world they would like you to come back. Ask them for books on the wider world, books that will tell you how other people live and work. And ask them for books about our Aborigines, and they will tell you about how long they have lived in this country, and how they were all over this land years ago.'

'Gosh! Bob, you're telling me so much, I wish my dad told me some of these things. Bob, I think I had better be going home now. My mum will be wondering where on earth I've been. And Bob, by the way, I have joined a library.'

'Come back when you can, son,' he said.

I headed back home. I cut down through the scrub, and where I could see the sea in the distance, there was blue all around and there were boats by the pier. The fishing boats always came back to the pier early in the morning and at the weekends I would come down early to see them. Bright colours on some of the boats, and big baskets full of fish, with their sad eyes staring off to nowhere, and men with big muscles throwing stuff around all over the place, with some loud talking and rough words as the sea caused the boats to rock gently up and down by the side of the pier. And on the clear calm days, the boats just sat there gently in the water with barely a ripple, with barely a sound. I liked the boats. There was always something to see, and there was always something that seemed to be happening.

Yet, when I came down onto the pier, all was quiet. There did not seem to be any movement on any of the boats. When I got close up, I could see little things happening. There were men cleaning fish and there were men doing some work with the nets. And there were others loading some fish into boxes which were then being loaded into a truck on the pier. There was movement, yet it almost appeared as if nothing was happening, but that was not the case at all. And sometimes the men would talk to me, because I went there most weekends. I used to wonder what it would be like to sail far out to sea on a big boat. I did not care much about the catching of the fish, although I knew that someone had to do it.

When I used to see the boats bobbing up and down by the pier, I used to wonder what it would be like to just sail off to far distance lands, to just sail away and stop for a night or two in strange ports. Or even to just sail around Australia like the famous explorers. And at night time, the boat would come into a little harbour which would protect it from the ocean storms and I would sit there having a cup of tea with some captain bloke and I would hear the water bobbing gently against the side of the boat, and there would be stars up in the sky, and the sky would be so clear, and the stars would be so bright that you would want to put your hand up and touch them. I know it would not always be like that, there would be danger sometimes, but that is the way I see it anyway. It was time to head back home. I knew Mum would be cross because I had been away far too long, far too long, which is always the way. I went back up onto the road from the pier and back into Tanti Avenue, past the houses where all the people behind windows were asleep in their dreams, past the trees and scrubs that stood still like soldiers with nowhere to go, and toys in gardens waiting for someone to pick them up and give them some joy and happiness.

On a cold Sunday morning, I decided to pay Bob a visit. The cold blew up the avenue at what must have been a thousand miles an hour and trees bent over so far that I thought they would soon touch the ground. Old people, wrapped in their Sunday best, bent themselves to the wind, determined to get to the church on time. I waved a greeting, gave them a smile, but they walked on, lost in the island of their thoughts. At the bottom of the avenue, the sea rushed to the shore as if there was some sort of hurry, and small boats bobbed about as if they had no right to be there, and hung on to their anchors like grim death, waiting and hoping the storm might go to sleep.

Huge waves battered the pier, and grim men in hats pulled well down clutched at fishing lines as if there might be something for them from the sea. An old man, clutching the arm of his wife as if she was his first ever girlfriend, bent himself to the wind. She clutched on to him, her face set grim on this wicked morning which drives men from the sea and people back to their homes. I turned up the track and headed toward Bob's shack. The banksia trees looked foreboding against the dark sky. I left the main track and headed down to Bob's place. I could smell smoke.

Down the track a bit, I came to some burnt grass. The fire had stopped at the edge of the path, but it had still burnt quite a bit of the bush. I came around the corner of the track leading down to Bob's place and found him sitting on a log. The hut had been burnt to the ground and he was sitting on the log scratching through some old books.

'They burnt it down. They burnt it down, the whole lot, the whole bloody lot. Sorry, son.'

'Who did this to you, Bob?' I asked.

'The vandals. Folks around here who don't like the likes of me, with my funny ways and things. They've tried it a few times, but I've always caught them and shooed them off. But this time they caught me short, as they say. I was down by the pier. They must have seen me going, because while I was there, I could see a bit of smoke up on the hill and I knew it must have been my place. They've burnt my books, some of my best books, some which I was thinking of lending to you, lad.'

'Bob, why do people do these things, why are there so many bad people around the place?'

'If I knew the answer to your question, I would probably be a rich man by now, that's for sure. I'm still trying to work it out. I'm not sure whether some folk are born bad or become bad. I've thought about it a lot. I still don't know the answer.'

He sat on a tree stump which had somehow missed the fire. He sat staring at his hands, looking at his palms, and then looking at his fingers as if he was going to make some great discovery. He sat there for quite a while; I lost all sense of time. At times, I thought he was going to say something, to tell me something about the fire, the damage, what he had lost, but he just kept sitting there staring at the ashes.

Then, after a while, he straightened his shoulders, raised his arm and shook his fist towards the town and said, 'I'll have my day with you lot, I'll have my day. Just you wait for old Bob, just you wait.' And then he slumped forward again and rested his elbows on his knees.

'Bob, where are you going to stay?'

'I'll be right, lad. I have a sister down the road a bit. She's on her own now so I'll be right with her. Her old man never thought much of me, but he shot through a few months ago, so I know I'll be okay there. Here's her address. Come down some time. It's not far from here.'

He scribbled her address for me on a bit of cardboard then ruffled his hands through my hair. Tears came to my eyes.

'Off you go now, lad, it's time to go now. Come and see old Bob down the track a bit. Not too soon, because I'll have to settle in a bit, but not too long either, there's things to talk about.'

'Okay, Bob.'

I wandered off and headed for home.

I had been away for a while. What was Mum going to say this time? My walks seemed to be taking longer. Each time I went out, I would go a bit further. See more things. Watch more people. Look at things and try to work out what is going on around the place. The sun was low in the sky and there was a little breeze blowing the leaves on the trees. I walked up the front path and through the front door into the hall.

'That you, son?' Mum called out from the kitchen at the end of the hall.

41

'Yes, Mum, it's me.'

'Where on earth have you been? Not off walking again down by the beach on your own, I hope? I have told you about it before. More than once, in fact.'

'I went for a walk. I met this nice man who had this little hut all by himself in the bushes.'

'You did what?'

'I met this man, like I told you. He had this great little hut and he lived there all by himself. And it was full of books and things, lots of beaut things. And he told me I must join a library, which I have done, and he was very pleased about that.'

Mum pursed her lips and her face went sort of all pale. She sat down on a chair next to the kitchen table.

'I have told you once if I have told you a thousand times, you do not speak to strangers and you do not speak to strange men. They can be dirty, that's what they can be, yes, dirty. And, what's more, some of them can even be what is known as undesirable. So that's all there is to it. I don't want you going off on any more silly walks. And as for books, there are plenty of them here. In fact, I found one the other day down by the side of the couch. Pictures as well too.'

'But Mum, Bob is not dirty, and he's not that other word you used either. He's a good man, and he doesn't yell at me and go crook at me like Dad does all the time. Anyway, I won't be going back to his hut because someone has burnt it down and he's going to live with his sister down the road.'

'Well, that's probably a blessing in disguise.'

'Mum, he was a good man. How can you talk about someone like you are doing if you've never met them? I don't understand you.'

'I just know, that's all, and there's nothing more to it. If he lives in a hut in the bush, like you say, why doesn't he live in a house like the rest of us, that's what I would like to know? He lives like he does because there'is something wrong with him, that's what I say, something wrong with him, not right in the upstairs department, as your father would say.'

'Mum, I think you're being cruel about someone you don't know, have never met, and are never likely to.'

Mum pursed her lips again. 'Well, Mr Smarty Pants, you're right there, right on the knocker. I most certainly will not be meeting him, or anyone else the likes of him. I know his sort, all that talk about books and stuff. And what a load of rubbish book reading stuff can be, that's what I say. Most of it is just rubbish, just rubbish, that's all there is to it.'

My mother got up from the table, looked at me with tears in her eyes, and walked down the hall to her bedroom and slammed the door shut.

I went to my room and cried my eyes out. In a few short weeks, my parents were back together again.

We were off to live in Clarinda.

Clarinda

I cannot remember how we came to get there, or what the motivation was in the first place. We shifted there on a corner site, where my father had built a cream-brick house with a shop in the front. There was an acre of land on which carnations were planted. I slept in a fibro sheeting sleepout which was quite a way from the house. It was a misery. We had chooks, but they did not lay much, and everywhere I looked there were market gardens. At night, you could smell the manure and during the day the dust rose from the paddocks. Some of the market gardeners used horses, some used machinery. Either way, the dust rose, sometimes in great clouds as the horses or the machinery moved between the furrows. And when a crop had been harvested, there was the smell of cabbage leaves as many of them were left to rot or they dug into the soil. Either way, they stank.

I mucked about at home a bit, and one day a truant officer came and spoke to my mum and the next thing I know I am off to school again, this time for my final year.

The country was flat. There was nothing to see and, again, I did not know a soul. There were sandpits. I found one with a sign which told you to keep out. I climbed the fence to have a look around. I walked around the edge of the pit. There was little vegetation and the edges were soft. There were a few small stones. I must have walked too close to the edge, because the next minute it had broken away and down. I slipped. It must have been the only scrub for miles because I managed to grab it on the way down and it stopped my fall. Down below, I could see a large area of sand with some bubbles coming up. There was another sign about quicksand. I found another pit where you could walk in and have a bit of a look around, so I did. I would sit there and throw stones in the water but then I found there were ducks in the water, so I stopped that and used to sit and watch them, and sometimes there were coots, and I knew they were coots because of the way their heads went backwards and forwards as they were going through the water.

There was talk of me going to work. I heard my parents talking about it. There was talk of the money I could bring in and how much I would receive for taking a suitcase full of carnations to Coles in Carnegie. I did not want to go to work, especially in a factory. I did not know what I wanted to do. All I knew was what I didn't want to do, it was that simple. But there was the talk, and my mother had gone all quiet again, and my father kept getting these frightful looks on his face, and his tongue kept going in and out and I did not like it. I think I was scared of him.

On the day he smashed the rake across my back, he had given me instructions to weed the carnations before taking them to Carnegie the next day. It had been a hot day, with no shade in the paddock. I started early because I knew it would be hot and there was a lot to do. My mum brought me some water during the morning and I came in for lunch for a while. Dust blew across the paddock during the afternoon and the heat did not give up. I did not like weeding, and I was no good at it. The heat became worse in the afternoon but I had to keep going.

There was a hedge on the edge of the block and I could see Mrs Walker from next door cutting the grass, as she was worried about the risk of fires in the summer months. Old Mr Walker, with one leg, as a result of the First World War, always sat in his chair under an old gum tree. I would wave to him and he would wave back with his crutch. I always liked to wave to Mr Walker, because he was a nice man. Mrs Walker would also wave and sometimes she would come over to the fence and talk to me. She did not like my father, so she always had a good look around our place before coming over. She wore a funny hat full of bird feathers and things, and little badges she picked up from shops. She told me, with a wink, that she had even paid for most of them. I thought that was funny, but I decided not to tell anyone.

If it was a hot day, she would take her hat off and hang it on the hedge for a while. She told me they had a farm up in the Mallee but they had to give it away because of Mr Walker's one leg and all that kind of thing. So they came to Clarinda and had been there for years. They had some back paddocks down and around the back of the house and they were going to grow something, she told me. I used to ask her what they were going to grow and she told me she had a book which told her everything she needed to know about growing things. But some of the words in the book she did not quite understand, and maybe I could help her one day, me being educated and having been to school. She told me she would bring the book over to the hedge one day when she saw me working in the paddock.

It was late in the afternoon. It was still hot and I had been working for hours. I had completed three rows of carnations; there were a couple to go and I was tired. I decided to have a bit of a rest. Dust flew all around as the wind had blown in from the south and I had dust in my eyes. I heard a rattle and I knew it was my father placing his bike against the shed. He came from around the back of the shed and headed towards me. When he got closer, I could tell he had been drinking. I had seen the look before.

'What are you doing sitting there?' he asked.

'I'm just having a rest. I'm tired, very tired,' I said.

'Tired, eh. I'll give you tired, you lazy little bastard.' He walked over to shed and grabbed the rake with the wooden handle. 'Tired, what a joke. I'll give you tired all right.' He raised the rake above his head.

At first, I was not sure what was going to happen. Then the rake crashed down across my back. Once, twice, three times, then the handle broke.

'Take that, you lazy little bastard. Work? You wouldn't know what work was if you fell over it. Get up and get on with it. I want the flowers to go to Carnegie in the morning.'

He left me on the ground and I could still smell the beer from him on my clothes. I do not know if I have ever hated anyone so much as my father. There were still a couple of hours of sunlight left, so I finished the rest of the furrows before dark. I was tired. I felt worn out. My back ached. I wondered whether he had broken something, but I think it was just heavy bruising. But I was sore, and it hurt to walk.

I went to my sleepout and slept for a while. I awoke to hear my mother screaming out, yelling at my father to leave the kids alone and calling him terrible names. I could hear him ranting and talking about his mother, a lady I was very fond of, and telling my mother she did not know what it was to be a mother like his mother, and if she dared to say anything against her, well, she would soon know all about that, don't you worry about that, you little Pommy slut.

'Why don't you pick on someone your own size?' I heard my mother say.

'I'll pick on anyone I like. All shapes and sizes, I'll take 'em all on, any time you like. I'm not weak, not like all you Poms, and all lousy stinking working man types you have in your bloody lousy family.'

I could hear Mum crying. It sounded like it came from deep inside her somewhere.

And there was another thing. There was this lady, a Mrs Groom. She lived with her husband over at the chook farm, just up the road. He was a nice man too. He grew whopping vegetables from all the manure he got from the chook farm. Mrs Groom was a nice lady; she often came over to our place to talk to Mum when my father was not there. I think she knew what was going on. I think there are some women who know about these things; at least, that's what I think anyway.

Anyway, we were sitting in the kitchen, Mrs Groom, my mother and me. It was nice day; the sun was shining through the window. Mum had cleaned up the kitchen a bit and had made some scones. I just sat there listening to them talking, not really taking much notice of what was going on. Outside, I could see the trees waving around a bit but after a while I got sick of looking at them. There was a rattle sound by the back door and my father came in. He came and sat at the end of the table.

'Bludging, eh?' he said, glaring at us.

'We're just having a cup of tea, that's all,' said my mum.

'That's all? What do you mean, that's all? Haven't you heard of work, good old work, good old elbow grease stuff that I was brought up on? And what about you, dearie, with your husband slaving up the road in that lousy chook house and coming home to you at night not smelling all nice in the bed for you.'

'Stop that, Les,' said my mum, angrily.

'It's all right, Alice,' said Mrs Groom, turning her back away from my father.

'Turning your back away from me, are you? Bet you don't turn your back at night when he wants a bit of something. What do you think about that now?'

'Les! Stop it. That's filthy talk in front of your son.'

'Filthy talk! I'll give you all filthy talk.'

Mrs Groom had bowed her head. Her shoulders were all hunched up and she had a handkerchief in her hand. She was wiping her eyes. There was a long knife on the table. I am not sure how it got there. Mrs Groom looked at my mum. My mum looked at Mrs Groom. My father picked up the knife. His tongue moved in and out of his mouth. There was saliva on his lips. His eyes were fixed on Mrs Groom. She stared at the table. He moved the knife around in front to him. He ran his fingers up and down the blade. He kept staring at Mrs Groom.

'I think I have to go, Alice,' she said, quietly.

'Running off, are we?'

'No, I just have to go, that's all.'

He put his hand on her shoulder and pressed her down into the chair. 'Not just yet, my lady, not just yet.'

There was quiet in the room.

He ran his fingers up and down the blade and twisted the blade in his hand. He kept staring out the window as if something was out there. There was nothing out there. He kept shifting in his seat and moving his feet on the floor. He kept scratching himself and then rubbing his hand over his unshaven face. He would look at Mrs Groom, then my mother and me, then give this funny smirk as if he had made some fantastic discovery about whatever was going on in his mind.

'You see, Mrs Groom, this is the way it is. It's like this. Nobody likes me all that much. Alice doesn't like me, and Barry and the other kids are working up to that. And I reckon the answer to all of it is that they're all jealous of me. Because, you see, I'm pretty strong. Anyone that gives me any lip, well, I just drop 'em, that's what I do, I just drop 'em. I take no cheek or lip from anyone, because I'm strong, that's what I am, I'm strong.'

'Yes, I'm sure you are, Mr Revill, I'm sure you are. Now, I have to be going now. My kids will be home from school soon.'

'Not so fast, sweetie, not so fast. And just you remember. Les is the name. Get it? Les is the name.'

Outside, the wind was getting up. I could see storm clouds through the window and the room had suddenly become much darker. Mum was looking anxious. She had a wet handkerchief in her hands. She kept moving it from her lap and then up to her mouth, from where she was making muffled cries. My father still sat at the end of the table. He held the knife firmly by the handle. Suddenly, he brought the point of the blade down on to the table. Saliva was coming from his mouth. Both Mrs Groom and my mother squealed out in horror.

'Gave you a bit of a fright, didn't I just, a real proper fright. I'm boss, you see, the real boss around this place, the boss cocky of the whole stinking show, that's what I am, the boss cocky of all of you. Now, Mrs Groom, there's no need for you to go just yet. Your kids will be just fine. We can all sit here and have a bit of a talk. Maybe we could play a game or two. Yes, that's what we could do: we can play some sort of a game. Maybe we could play a game of one of you trying to take this here knife off me. Now, that would be a great game. What do you all think about that now?'

'Les, stop it!' said Mum, her hand to her face.

'I have to go home,' said Mrs Groom. 'The kids will be waiting for

49

me soon, and hubby will be home from work and he will want to know where I am and all.'

'Well, what a shame, what a real shame, him having to wait and all. What with you slaving over here half the day drinking tea, yapping, and him working his guts out to keep you in whatever he keeps you in.'

'Les, stop it, will you, just stop it. Why are you carrying on like this? What's got into you? Are you mad or something?' said Mum, wringing her handkerchief yet again.

'Mad, am I?' And he grabbed the knife more firmly in his hand and started to wave it around in front of himself. And then he pointed it at Mrs Groom, then my mother, then me.

I could feel my hands shaking. Mum's lips were trembling and Mrs Groom looked very pale.

'Mad, am I? Is that what you said? I'll give you mad. By crikey, that's what I'll do to you lot. Calling me names and all that stuff. And you, Mrs Smart Arse Groom from the chook yard up the road, who the hell do you think you are coming over here and wasting our time with all your female yapping stuff? Female yapping stuff, that's what it is, female yapping stuff, from way back.'

And then he went all sort of quiet as if he had suddenly had some great thought. His face went pale and he had a distant look on his face which looked really odd. I did not like it at all. He stared at each of us, one after the other. Saliva still dribbled from his mouth. He kept staring at my mother. Then he would stare at Mrs Groom. Then he stared at me. Then he would rock backwards and forwards on his chair and give little mumbles.

Outside, I could see how the clouds had billowed up and had become darker. I could see the pine trees next door bending right over and there was dust in the air coming in from the paddocks. The road next to our place had not been made. Dust and small stones blew into our place from the road and I could hear the stones hitting the back door. It was a bad storm, which often happened around springtime.

My father had gone quiet. The knife lay in his open hand on the table. It was as if he were asleep. I slowly reached across the table and started to gently remove the knife from his hand. He gave a sudden jump. Terrified, I pulled my hand back. He muttered something about his mother, and then mumbled something else I did not understand. He seemed to drift off again. I looked to my mum and Mrs Groom for some sort of support and they both nodded in my direction. Mrs Groom was still very pale. I slowly moved my hand across the table again. I put my hand around the blade and slowly eased it from his hand. The handle slid from his palm. He did not make a sound. I took the knife, opened the back door, and threw it as far as I could.

Mrs Groom and my mum just sat looking at each other.

'I'd better go now, while I can,' said Mrs Groom, looking towards the door.

'Call in, any time,' said Mum. 'It's not always like this, thank God!'

Uncle Joe and the Wardrobe

Uncle Joe liked a drink. He was my mum's brother. He worked at a factory down in South Melbourne but I never found out where. You did not ask questions like that. He would come and stay with us for a few weeks and then he would disappear for a while and then just turn up again. When he turned up, Mum would mutter something, look at the ceiling and then just get on with things as if he had never been gone in the first place. He shared the sleepout with me. He did not wash much. In fact, he stank more than a bit, and Mum used to mutter things to him about his underwear. But Uncle Joe did not mind. He was a happy soul, seemingly content within himself and, like a lot of men, used to his own company – a mumbler.

I could never quite understand what he was mumbling about. He was sitting on the step one day outside the sleepout. I was going through the motions of trying to look like I was doing some weeding.

He was mumbling. 'Bloody women, bloody women. Should never have met that Doris woman, should never have met her!' he said, staring off into space. 'Spent two whole quid on her last night, two whole quid, and what does she give me in return? Some long bulldust story about having a headache and she wants an early night. Two whole quid, for crying out loud! Never touch 'em, son, never touch 'em. They're more trouble than they're worth, that's for sure.'

He rambled on. He blew his nose a couple of times and scratched himself between the legs and he seemed to settle down a bit. After a while, he got up off the step, gave me a wink, muttered something about going out for a bit of a drink and wandered down the path. He could have been going anywhere; I did not have a clue.

I went to bed early that night. It was a cold night and the wind was up and I was glad to get under the warm bedclothes. The wind cast strange shadows on the wall and after a while I found myself drifting in and out of sleep. Eventually, I drifted off. I do not know what time it was when I woke up again, but with the curtains drawn, and no moon, my room was pitch-dark. There was a strange series of noises coming from the area where there was a large wardrobe in the far corner. There was a crashing sound and what appeared to be the noise of someone falling over and then struggling to their feet again.

'I found it, I found it, I've found the bloody door!'

It was Uncle Joe. Into the wardrobe he went, followed by a crashing sound as he pulled the door shut behind him. There was the sound of flowing liquid. Then a loud fart.

'Phew!' said Uncle Joe. 'Didn't think I was going to make it to the dunny for a while.'

In the morning he woke up, bright as button. The sleepout stunk of pee, as did the wardrobe.

Get the Bags Out, Harry!

The grass on the Walker place next door had been drying out for months. There had been heavy winter rains. On many market gardens, there had been heavy flooding between the furrows. During the early spring, I could see the ground of the Walker place drying out. Mrs Walker did not say all that much, but she knew the ground was drying out. Her kids knew the ground was drying out as well. That is the way of things; that is the way things go.

By the middle of spring, the grass had grown higher. It had also grown drier. Some days, there were high winds, and on those days, dry leaves were blown towards the timber walls of the house and some blew underneath, because some of the timber had been used for firewood. Some people have to do that. In December, there was a small fire up by the school, but folks put it out pretty smartly. Then in late January things got drier again. Mrs Cooper, down the road, had a small quick fire the other side of the machinery shed, but she was on to it, so she reckoned she had done a pretty good job.

But March was different. People felt different. They looked different. Folks coming in and out of the local store had little to say. They did not stop to talk. There was no time to talk. In March, the winds got up. The dust blew off the road into our place and I reckoned the chooks went all funny. The track into the Walker place had never been cleared of dry leaves, and the grass was high leading right up to their place. The kids did little, except Harry. Mr Walker did little because one of his legs was over in France somewhere because of a little thing he called the first world whore. I never understood the joke, and he never bothered to explain. So Harry and Mrs Walker did the lot, and Mr Walker sat in a chair by the back door and rolled cigarettes all day and patted the dog when he got a chance. There were pine trees close to their house and a couple of gum trees as well. I did not know much about fires, but I told Harry one day, when I saw him up at the store, that maybe someone should get rid of some of those trees. He mumbled something.

In the last week of March, there was a large build-up of clouds. On the Wednesday afternoon, the wind became stronger, the clouds built up, it became very dark, and then there was a lightning strike. The strike hit the damp ground by the Walker front gate, where there was a bit of a creek. The trees by the front gate caught fire and the fire spread to the dry grass and headed towards the Walker place and the place next door.

Mrs Walker came out of the house and stood looking at the fire. I was standing by our wire fence. I could see she looked angry. She was a small woman. She was of a stocky build, with strong-looking arms. She stood with her legs apart and her hands on her hips. She had on an old hat. She looked up towards our place. My father was standing on the back veranda. He was looking at the fire. He did not move. I climbed under the fence and went to help Mrs Walker.

'Get the bags out, Harry, get the bags out,' she cried out.

'Okay, Mum,' he cried back.

'Wet them first, Harry, wet them first, for crying out loud!'

'Okay, okay!'

The fire had jumped the creek by the front fence. It was a grass fire, moving fast. The wind changed and the fire headed towards our place. Then the wind changed quickly again and headed back towards the Walkers' place. My father kept standing on the veranda. He did not move. Mr Walker came out from the house on his crutches. He carried a wet bag. I wondered how he was going to move with his one leg. He moved fast. He was a big man with broad shoulders and he took to the fire head-on. He was able to swing the bag over his shoulder and bring the bag down on to the fire, which had got into some low scrub near some blackberries. He put it out and then slowly limped his way back to the house.

I gave them a hand. I grabbed a spare bag lying on the ground. The air was hot. The wind had got up again, and there was dust swirling on the track leading towards the house. Mrs Walker was over by the blackberries where Mr Walker had been. Harry was giving her a hand. I only had on a pair of shorts. I could feel the heat on my legs. Where the fire went into the longer grass, there was a sudden burst of flame and I had to retreat quickly. The fire was heading up the track and I could see it would soon reach the house.

My father was standing on the veranda. My mum came out and yelled at him. He yelled back. He raised his fist. She picked up a lump of wood from the floor of the veranda. He stood there and I could just make out his tongue going in and out, which it always did when he was angry. He did not move. Mum did not move. Then he walked down the steps and went down the yard towards the chook house. He did not look back. He made no effort for Mrs Walker. She called out to me and Mum for more help. Mrs Walker was standing in the middle of the paddock crying her eyes out. She was covered in ash and dust. The fire was nearly at the long grass by the house. Mr Walker was sitting on his chair by the house, his good leg stretched out in front of him. He was covered in dust and ash. One of his arms hung limply by his side. His hat was singed. He was yelling as the fire came towards him. Mum and I grabbed a couple of bags from our place, wet them in a trough by the back door and headed for the fire. Mrs Walker joined us and the three of us got between the fire and the house, the dry timber house. There was a drop in the wind. Things seemed to go quiet. Mrs Walker said it was when we should really have a go at it, so we did.

I have never seen two women work so hard. One after the other, Mrs Walker and my mum brought the wet bags down on to the fire and I joined them as best I could. The wind stayed down. We pushed the fire back. There were a couple of buckets of sand, so we threw them into the path of the fire as well. The sun was setting. We could see we were getting the better of the fire. It was dying down. We kept using the bags. We found some more sand. Mr Walker yelled out to us and told us what a good job we were doing. I felt useful. I felt as if I was achieving something for somebody.

We had forgotten about Harry. He had been down by the creek and the long grass by the front of the place. He came towards us. His legs were burnt, as was his face.

'I stopped it, Mum,' he said. 'I stopped it.'

Aunty Alma, the Flying Aunty

It was a family party with the family members from my father's side. There was his brother, with his wife and kids, and there were distant uncles and aunts who my mother said had just been let out of the zoo. Some looked strange to me. Their faces looked funny, and when they spoke, they put together a couple of sentences and then went all sort of quiet. Mum said if I got three sentences, I was doing well. She had only managed about six from Aunty Alma in twenty-five years.

Uncle Col, he stood in the corner holding a beer. Every so often, he would lean backwards and forwards on his heels and toes and I could have sworn he was going to fall flat on his face. Then he would straighten up, blink, top up his beer from a bottle on the table next to him, and then blink again. My father went over to him and had a lengthy conversation which must have lasted for at least a minute or two. Then Uncle Col did some more staring and blinking, and a bit more backwards and forwards on the heels and toes.

Aunty Jean was on the floor drinking sherry from a tin mug. She was lying back against the wall with her skirt up around her knees and her legs open. My mum told me to stop looking and to come out into the kitchen and have a lamington. I had a lamington and then went back to have a look at the legs of Aunty Jean. I had a look for a bit of a while, no more than about twenty minutes, then went back into the kitchen for another lamington. My father had some distant relation up against the wall and was telling him all about the Poms and Germans, and just about any other race he could think of. They both were smoking, and what with my father pressing him against the wall, both of their cigarettes were joined in the middle and every so often a long curl of ash would head for the floor.

Uncle Bert did not look so good. I could see him edging slowly to the back door. Then he made a bolt for it, stood on the dog, and headed off down the back steps to the gully trap. There was a frightful sound, so Mum put on a record of Richard Tauber, and Aunty Alma said it was the worst music she had ever heard in her life, and she wanted to hear something sexy. My mum told her to wash her mouth out and not to come round to our place with all her dirty talk, especially when there were children around the place.

Aunty Alma filled her glass and then told my mum she would say what she liked, where she liked, and bugger the children. And, what's more, bugger the Poms as well, now she had come to think of it. Mum went quiet, not a good sign. My father had heard the conversation and he had gone all quiet as well. In fact, the whole room had gone quiet, so I thought it best to sit on the floor in the corner out of the line of fire. My father came and stood in front of Aunty Alma. I did not like the look on his face. She kept staring at him, he kept staring at her. She asked him what the hell was he staring at, and he said he was wondering that himself, and had worked out that it was something the cat had brought in from the local tip. Aunty Alma kicked him in the shins, and then threw her beer in his face. If the room was quiet before, it was deadly quiet now. Not a sound. I crouched down low on the floor. Then there was this whacking sound and a curse from Aunty Alma. My father had hit her right on the jaw. She sailed backwards across the room and landed right next to me. Her false teeth popped out. She vomited into her lap. She said some terrible things and my mother put her fingers in her ears meaning I should do the same. She stank. She was rotten drunk.

My father was standing in the middle of the room waving his fist around. He yelled out, 'I gave her the old one two. The old one two, you can't beat it,' he said, waving his fist around again.

People were quiet. I heard someone saying something about going home. Aunty Alma was still on the floor. My mother went over to her to help her up. I heard her saying something about getting cleaned up and looking respectable.

'Leave her alone,' yelled my father. 'Leave her alone, I say. Leave her alone, the bitch.'

'Shut up!' said Mum.

My father raised his fist, and then drew his arm back.

'Don't even think about it, not even once, you drunken sod of a man,' said my mum.

He stood swaying on his feet. His fist was clenched. He moved his fist around to his front and then down to his side. His face was flushed. My mother was helping Aunty Alma to her feet. He moved towards her, raising his fist. Uncle Joe stepped between them. He had been a boxer at the West Melbourne Stadium. My father lunged at Uncle Joe. My father was not a boxer. He did not move quickly on his feet. He did not know how to weave and duck. He moved towards Uncle Joe and threw two wide punches. Neither of them landed. He stood back and came in again. He threw another punch and it caught Uncle Joe on the shoulder. Then another wild punch hit Uncle Joe just above the eye. That was the last thing my father could remember for some little time.

Uncle Joe planted his feet firmly in front of my father. There was a heavy grunt from my father as the first punch went deep into his belly. Then, two quick but hard punches to the jaw, followed by what looked like a whopping uppercut. My father went reeling back across the kitchen table, which had been laid out with supper plates, cakes, cups of tea, scones, and plates full of Swiss rolls and lamingtons. He went right across the table and landed in the corner on the other side, banging his head on the corner of the fireplace. He was out to it.

'Well, I never,' said my mum.

'Strewth!' said Aunty Alma.

'He looks poorly,' said someone else.

My father started to rouse up. He propped himself up on one elbow and felt his jaw. He looked around the room. He sat up. He slowly got to his feet and leaned against the wall. He did not look good. 'You lot think you are all pretty smart, don't you? Well, I've got news for all youse lot. That's for sure, that's for mighty sure. Just you wait and see, just you wait and bloody see. Just a bunch of lousy bloody Poms, the lot of you. Why don't you all hop on the next boat back to Pommy land, with your stupid king and all those green hills you keep banging on about?'

The fact that most of the people in the room were from his side of the family and came mostly from Colac was lost on him.

He kept leaning against the wall. He held his hand over his belly and then he would feel his jaw. He bent over. Then he vomited. The vomit went on to the edge of the table and down the wall. He stared around the room.

'There now, see what you've all made me do, see what a mess I've made. Not my fault, not my fault at all. It's the way you all treat me, that's what it is, it's the way youse all treat me. Not fair, that's what it is, not fair, not fair at all.'

'Stop moaning,' someone muttered.

'For God's sake, stop your moaning and clean up your mess. Get the bucket and mop from the wash house,' Mum said.

'Do it your bloody self,' he said.

I sat on the floor; it seemed the best and safest place to be. I could see legs going past, then more legs, some with trousers, some with skirts or dresses. Sometimes, the skirts or dresses stood next to a pair of trousers for a while and then they both wandered out into the backyard for quite a while. This would be replaced with another pair of legs and dresses and after a short while they wandered off to the backyard as well. Too cold, I thought, to be going out into backyards at this time of the year.

In the morning, all was quiet. I got up about seven a.m. and fed the chooks. There was the smell of vomit in the kitchen. Dust blew across our backyard from the market garden over the road. There was a strong smell of manure. My father came into the kitchen. He did not speak. My mother came in. She did not speak.

Later in the day, I went out to my sleepout and sat on the steps. It was a nice day, not too hot, just nice.

After a while, my mum came out and sat next to me. She put her arm around me. 'It's like this, son,' she said, 'things are tough. This joint is not working out as we expected, or at least how your father expected, that's for sure. So the thing is, you're going to have to start working. There's a job for you at the woollen mills down in Bentleigh. It's from seven in the morning till five at night, and they'll pay you a bit over two pound a week. That will be very handy, and you can keep a few bob for yourself as well.'

'But I don't want to go to work, least of all in some stupid woollen mill down the road. I'll have to leave here on my bike at about six thirty in the morning. It's crazy, just crazy. If I study more at school, and work a bit harder with my homework, well, then, I can pass my exams, maybe down the road, go on to the tech school, maybe even the university.'

'Now, don't go getting above yourself, son. The university's not for the likes of us. We're working folk, and once you're working folk, well, you're always working folk, that's the way it is, that's the way it will always be.'

'Mum, you're so wrong, just so wrong.'

'Well, anyway, son, that's the way it is. I've been to the factory and spoke to the very nice manager there and you can start next Monday. Your father said he'll fix your bike for you.'

'Thanks,' I said. 'Thanks.'

I started on the Monday morning. The factory was called Centenary Woollen Mills. My father had fixed my bike and a few minutes down the road the chain came off. I fiddled and mucked about and managed to get things right, but my hands were now covered in grease from the chain. It was about six thirty. It was cold. I had only one jumper at home and I could not find it when getting dressed. There was no time for breakfast; I had to start at seven a.m. sharp. They called me a bobbin boy. My job was to clean the bobbins before they went on to the knitting machines. The foreman was Vic Weston. He fancied himself as an opera singer, so he would walk up and down the aisles between the machines singing all these crazy opera songs I did not know from Adam.

He wore a grey coat and a collar and tie and when he spoke his bottom teeth jumped up and down and I had trouble keeping a straight face.

At that time in the morning, there was little traffic on the road. There were market gardens either side of the road and the strong smell of manure and blood and bone. Mist hung around the paddocks and on to the road. The only sound I could hear was the sound of my bike. The road rose past the paddocks and there were golf links on either side of the road. There were tall pine trees and through the trees I could see the clubhouse, and I thought the clubhouse looked pretty posh. It was getting light and I could see some early golfers standing under some trees. I think they were waiting for it to lighten up a bit before they started to play. As I found out later, the mist always collected in the lower parts of the road and I had to watch out for the odd car as I did not have a light.

I hated going to work. I did not want to. I had no idea what I wanted to do, only a vague idea of what I did not want to do. I wanted an education, maybe to learn some sort of a trade. Maybe a schoolteacher? I did not know. I asked my father once whether I should be an accountant. For whatever reason, he gave me a hard whack across my ear and told me to stop being an idiot. I worked out that if you are told you are an idiot for long enough, then it starts to grow on you and you start to think like the way you think an idiot thinks, and the whole rotten business just becomes part of you. I did not like it at all.

I arrived at the factory just before seven. A Mr Johnson was waiting for me just inside the door from where I put my bike.

'Hello, son. My, you are young, aren't you? Something tells me you should still be at school and not coming to this joint every day. Anyway, that's the way it looks to me, but it's none of my business and I'm sure your parents know what they are doing. Come with me now and I'll take you down to where you'll be working. The whistle will blow at ten for morning tea, so keep your ears peeled as it gets close to the time.'

He took me down through rows of noisy machines. There were mainly women working the machines. They did not seem to notice me as I walked past. I could not get over the noise. It was terrible. Men were pushing large bales of wool on trolleys which looked very heavy for them. I reckon they would have weighed a thousand tons, but I did not know much about weights and things. There was music playing above the noise of the machines. There were men walking up and down in grey coats and noting something down in little notebooks, with a pencil with a bit of rubber on the end.

We arrived at the section I was to work in. I was introduced to Vic Weston, the foreman. He also had a grey coat, and in the top pocket he had a little notebook and next to that he had a little pencil with a piece of rubber on the top. I thought to myself that the best job in this place is to have a grey coat with a top pocket, with a notebook and a pencil, with a bit of rubber on the top. He shook my hand. His handshake was limp, a bit like a rag doll on a bad day. Then he walked away and stood at the end of the machines looking at me. I did not know what to do so I stood there looking at him as well.

He sort of puffed up his chest. I thought he looked like one of our roosters before he starts chasing one of the hens. Then he started to sing one of these opera things which I had heard on the wireless one day over in my sleepout at home. He waved his arms around and went very red in the face and I thought he was going to explode and make a mess all over the place. One of the ladies working on the machine, well, she gave me wink and then a nod towards Vic. Then she moved her fingers around and around by the side of her head. I am sure she thought Vic was bonkers or something like that.

Then he stopped all that singing business and came back down the machine to me. 'I'm the boss of this section, you see, you see,' he said, and his bottom teeth jumped up and down.

I started to laugh.

'Are you laughing at me?'

'No, sir, I'm not,' I said, trying to keep a straight face, which was not easy.

'That's okay then. Because I won't have it, do you hear, won't have it, and that's all there is to it, do you hear?'

I thought he was never going to stop. And then, over the next many weeks, I came to understand he was not well. The ladies on the machines made a little spot for him in a corner around the back of one of the machines. It was out of the way and could not be seen from one of the manager's windows, which looked down onto most of the machine areas.

Vic would have a sleep, usually in the afternoons, then he would wake up and check that I had cleaned all the bobbins okay. He would check them all and see that I had not made too much mess around the place, that I had done some sweeping up and that the areas between the machines were clean and tidy for the ladies to walk up and down for their work. Then he would walk up and down the machines with his hands behind his back, refreshed after having been asleep for a couple of hours. He would walk up between the line of machines and it was always just after three p.m. The ladies would give each other a wink, then they would give me a wink, and we would all make sure we were standing as near as possible to attention, without actually looking like it.

He would pat me on the back when he reckoned I had done a good job. Or a gentle and not unfriendly clip behind the ear if things did not look too good. I liked Vic. He was good to me. He treated me fairly. I think he must have been told something about my father. Or maybe he had been told something about why I was at work so young. There was something wrong about it. Other kids were still at school. One kid a bit older than me was off learning how to be a builder, or something like that.

It was an early start. It was always a rush to get there. I often hopped on my bike without breakfast because there were times when Mum was tired or there was not much food lying around the place. That is the way it was. That is how things go. By about nine a.m., I was starving. The ladies on the machines knew. They would bring in cakes. They had this little tray which they kept down on the floor between the machines. Once they knew Vic was out of the way for a bit, they would load the tray up with little cakes and a soft drink. There were a couple of big crates in the corner and a tiny table, and I was able to squeeze in there and have myself a feed a couple of times a week.

The factory was owned by Stanley Korman. It was as modern as tomorrow. There was a full-time nursing sister, a hairdressing salon and a crèche for young children. The union man came around on his bike. He was a little bloke. He parted his hair down the middle and he had a whopping big nose. He used to stand on a box in the lunchroom and talk about going on strike. I did not have a clue what he was talking about. He got thrown out by some of the men more than once.

I was treated well at the factory. The ladies looked after me. They were kind. I liked the German lady. She used to bring me in little cakes and what she called strudel. I loved it, had never had anything like it. She told me about the bombing of Hamburg, the dead people in the streets, the fires, the firestorms, and people being burned alive, the sheer desolation of it all. One morning, after we had been talking for a while, she started to cry. I did not know what to do, so I put my arm around her. I held her close and she kept sobbing and sobbing. After a while, she said she felt better. She brushed herself down and went back to her machine.

I liked talking to the German lady. She told me about her country and how she lived in a little village close to the high alps. In the evenings, she would walk to the end of the town and up on the grassland which leads to the lower parts of the alps. She would sit there and watch the colours changing across the higher peaks as the sun went down. Her parents told her that war was coming and how she must be ready for it. She did not want war. She hated war. She remembered her grandfather, and what he was like after the First World War.

The German Grandfather of the Lady Who Made Strudel

People in the family used to tell her all about him before he went away to the war. He used to sing. He would play the guitar and the piano and sing the most beautiful songs about love, and songs about the mountains and the high peaks. He was a young man. He was a happy man. And then he married the young girl from the village. He told just about anyone who was prepared to listen that he was the happiest man in the whole world. And, within a year or so, a baby son was born. And on clear sunny mornings, he would go with his wife and the young baby for walks up the gentle alpine tracks, which would lead them to a grassy meadow. And they would sit there on the warm grass with the alpine flowers coming into bloom and they thought there could not be a better place to be in the whole world.

And then the war came. He went away. He was away for nearly four years. When he came home, the village welcomed him. There was a big party in the village hall. The mayor came, and all the business folk, and his old headmaster from his school. They sang songs of welcome, and speeches were made, and there was beer and nice cakes, and his wife looked happy, and his son looked as if he was wondering who this strange man was who kept kissing his mother. And then they asked him to talk, to make a little speech. He started to talk. He said a few words. He thanked everyone for the nice welcome they had given him. And then he sat down. He could say no more. The room went quiet. Some people muttered a few words and then they went quiet as well. The light had gone from his eyes. The smile had gone from his face. The mayor gave him a guitar and asked for a song. He told the mayor he could not sing, he would not sing, and he would never sing again.

He told his wife they must go now.

And on the clear mornings when the sun was shining, he would sit at the end of the path by his little vegetable patch. It was a small area. He kept it neat and tidy. There were cabbages and herbs, and it was all that he wanted. He did not laugh, he did not smile, and when his son came down the path to see him, he stared at his son until the tears filled his son's eyes, and the boy walked away back up the path to the kitchen.

But the nights were the worst. The nights of the sweats. The nights of the dreams. The nights when the room in which he slept was somehow not the room in which he slept but some faraway place he could never recognise. He would wake up and lie on his back and stare at the ceiling, and he knew his wife was doing the same. He could hear her soft breathing and he knew she wanted him to touch her, to caress her, to give her the loving she missed in the long dark nights on her own. But he could not touch her, could not love her, and then he would feel her rolling over to her side of the bed, and he could hear the soft sobs of her breathing as she cried further into the night.

But when he closed his eyes, all he could hear was the sound of men screaming. And when the British came into their trenches with their deadly bayonets, with the grins on their faces as they thrust the bayonets deep into the men on either side of him, he was yet to work out how they missed him. But miss him they did. And they stood smoking at the end of the trench, and they were laughing and joking a lot, and when one of his friends raised his arm and cried out in pain a British soldier went to him and jabbed his bayonet deep into the throat of the man. And if any of the men on the ground moved, then they jabbed them again because that is what they wanted to do. That is what they were trained to do.

And he stayed there for a night and a day, and for another night, and then he started to make his way back through the lines to the medical tent. Men stared at him and he stared back. He could hear them saying things, but the voices had no meaning. There were sounds, but he could not discern one sound from another. The officer at the medical tent looked down his throat and shone a light into his eyes and told him to go back to the front and to behave like a man. He told him about how important his job was, and how important it was to fight, and, yes, to die if necessary. He did not want to die; he did not want to feel the bayonet in his guts. He had heard the screams of the men. He had heard them die. He had seen them die. He had seen the looks on their faces as the steel went into them and he did not want to die this way, he could not die this way, he could not. That is what he was thinking when they found him by one of the trenches. That is what he was telling them as they led him away.

He had been taught to be proud. To honour his country, his officers, his fighting unit. He had been taught that the British soldiers were poor fighters, how they became afraid very easily, how they would run from the knife or the bayonet. That is what he had been told. That is what he believed. And in the early days, nothing much seemed to happen. One day, when nobody was looking, he waved to a British soldier. The soldier waved back. He thought it a hell of a joke, all the waving business.

Then things changed, on both sides. There was the gas. Both sides blamed the other. Someone muttered something about the rules of war, how it was not the right thing to do, using gas on people. And then he saw men after a grenade had hit them. He saw them with half a face or lying out there in no-man's-land with their guts hanging out all over the place, and the man trying to hold his guts inside himself while he tried to crawl back to the lines. And the man who was shot in the groin, he had only been married three months when he came away. This man stared a lot. He did not talk much. He just stared. He muttered things about how he could not go home to his young wife now, not the way he was now, not the way he was, down there, as he called it.

So, one night, with a full moon, and when there had been little firing from the other side, he just climbed over the edge of the trench and walked towards the British lines. We called out. We abused him. We called him dirty stupid names. We asked him to think about his wife, to think about his mother, but he walked on. And then there was just one single shot and he dropped, just like that, one single shot. But he got up slowly and kept walking towards them, and then he copped two more shots and that was it. He dropped and stayed there and did not move at all. That is what happened. One minute he was alive and kicking, talking about this, talking about that, moaning about his groin, worried about the young wife at home, how she would probably get herself a boyfriend to keep her happy. All that stuff. And then he would stare. They all stare. I stare, they stare. We all stare. If we could arrange for all the Poms and Germans to stare on the same day, not a shot would be fired.

And then there was the night without the moon. We moved slowly over the open ground, but we kept low, and we stopped quite a few times and lay on the ground. We were to attack the British in their trenches. We were ready to do it; we had seen and heard what they had done to our men. We had our bayonets fixed. We were ready. We waited for a while. We could hear voices coming from the other side of the parapet. We could hear a bit of laughter and a bit of singing. I thought some of the songs had the same tunes as ours. I thought it was a bit funny. We moved slowly across the open ground. It was a dark night. There was heavy cloud and some light rain. Our officer waved his hand for us to be quiet. We moved a bit closer: the singing became a bit louder and then there would be some more laughter and then a bit more singing.

Our officer gave us the signal to stop. We lay on the ground. The British were just a few feet away from us. They were quiet. We were quiet. Our officer raised his hand and we knew when he suddenly dropped it that it was the time to go. We watched him. The moon came out from behind the clouds and he dropped his hand. It was time to go. The trench was not very deep so some of us came over the top while others came in at the end. There were eight of them, twelve of us. A couple of them were kids, about sixteen. They were reaching for their rifles when we came upon them. We used the bayonet and there were screams I do not want to hear again. There are sights I do not want to see again. I do not want to see those eyes popping as the steel goes in. I do not want to hear them calling out for their mothers as they lay there groaning. I do not want to have to go amongst them again to finish them off, to stop the moaning and look at the staring eyes.

And when it was over, and we had finished them off, our officer stood there with a great big grin on his face. And he just stood there, looking at us, looking at the young kids in the trench, with the smell of shit, the staring eyes. His smile went away. He crouched down and he started to shake all over, and he swore like I have never heard a man swear before and we all looked at each other because we did not know what to do, because he was our officer, he was our leader.

We sat there for a while, not sure how long, but we sat there. We were waiting for our officer to say something, to do something, but all he did was sit and look at the bodies on the floor of the trench. The sky was starting to lighten up. It was the early dawn. It was time to leave. The officer stood up. It was time to go. He told us to be quiet. He told us to respect the dead, especially the young dead. He led us out of the trench and we kept low as we headed back to our lines. The sun was coming up and there was a stench in the air. There were dead animals and there were maggots. I did not like it. We reached our lines.

A shell had landed at the far end of the trench where some of our men who had arrived to relieve us were sheltering. There were about eight of them. It had been a direct hit. It must have been a big shell. There was not much left of them. There was some moaning and we got one of them out. His arm was gone and half of his face was missing. We took him back through the lines as best we could, but he did not look good and all he could do or say was to scream and mumble and talk about his little village back home. We took him back to the medical area and we left him there. As we went back through the lines, we could hear his screams as they started to treat him. That is what we heard.

The German Lady's Friendship at the Woollen Mills in Bentleigh

So that is what the German lady told me at work. Sometimes, I would have lunch with her. We would sit on a couple of boxes down behind the machines. I would go to the canteen and get a couple of cups of tea and bring them back for us. She told me, again and again, how much she liked the bush here, and the bright sunshine. I did not know what to say to her. I did not know what to talk about. She asked me did I have a girlfriend and I told her I did not. Come to think of it, and I told her this, I don't think I had many other friends either. She told me how important it is to have friends. Many of her friends were killed in the war or left behind in Germany.

She used to muck up her sentences. She used to get her words back to front, so I would help her with it a bit. Not that I knew much about this English stuff. She had a sister on the other side of town and she had a husband with whom she used to fight like mad. He did not like Australia: hated the bush, did not like our beer, and the women did not have any bums. I told her I thought that was pretty rude and she said she told her husband that all the time, but it still did not make any difference.

She told me about the picnic they had a few weeks previously. She had packed up some things, some strudel, some nice cakes and some hot water in a thermos for some coffee. She even had some beer in a container with some ice around it to keep it nice and cold. They drove out through Ringwood, then on to Lilydale, then to Healesville. Then they went further north over the Black Spur. She told me about the beautiful tall gums as the road followed the contours up the spur. The road was narrow, so they had to drive slowly, and her husband kept moaning about the road. He did not like narrow roads and he did not like the twisting and turning, and sometimes when he came around a corner, the sun got in his eyes, and he did not like that much either. They reached the top of the spur and found a spot amongst the tall trees for lunch. She spread a blanket on to the ground and made the lunch. Her husband said he could have sworn he saw a snake which must have been at least ten feet long. He discovered there were ants.

She told me how she enjoyed the peace of the bush. She told me how it was a feeling she did not have in Germany, not to the same extent anyway. She felt as if she was at peace with herself, she felt a sense of calm. But her husband kept moaning, so she went and sat by herself for a while. There was a little creek running down through a gully. There were ferns and some small wattles hanging low over the creek. And there were some larger rocks and the water had made a sort of track around the big rocks and there were little pools where the water started to make its way further down the mountain. And she saw all that. She called out to her husband to come and join her, to come and listen to the water coming down over the rocks. He turned his head away and ignored her.

She waved to him to catch his attention. She wanted to show him the little creek. But he did not move. So she sat there. There was gentle shade from some overhanging trees. There was a slight breeze coming up from the valley below. She could see down into the valley, where there were a couple of farms with a few sheep under a tree. She had never known such peace. She could see her husband sitting with his arms folded. He had packed up all the lunch things and had put on his coat. He was ready to go home.

What is it with men? She had not known many men; in fact, her husband was the only man she had slept with. But she imagined or tried to imagine what another man would be like. What he would be like to sleep with. Would he love her deeply and kindly? Would he talk to her? Would she feel like talking to him? She wondered all that as she observed the bush and reflected on the few years they had been together from which the marriage had not produced a child. Most of the time she did not enjoy their lovemaking. It was all too quick, too rough. Some nights, he hurt her. Maybe, she thought, it was the way it was meant to be. She was not sure.

She walked down and sat by the edge of the creek. There were ripples as the water went over the river stones and she could see pretty colours of quartz and other bright stones. A little further on, the creek cascaded down into a deep, shaded pool. There were low branches hanging over it and she could see that where the trees were hanging over the pool it was very shady, but the centre of the pool was in bright sunshine. One day, on my own, I will come back here for a swim, she thought.

She walked back up to her husband.

'What's down there? Where have you been?' he asked.

'I have been looking at the little creek.'

'Madness,' he said, 'madness.'

They packed the car. He slammed the boot down. They drove back down the Spur and through the suburbs to home.

The Inescapable Factory

There were another couple of young boys in the factory, but I never got to know them all that well. They sort of kept to themselves a bit and I did not like it all that much. I liked Mrs Dean. She was a Scottish lady. Her husband played the accordion, and he used to go off to all of these dances on a Saturday night playing all of these lovely Scottish dance songs. So she told me about all it, and she told me all about Scotland, and the high hills, which were not all that high, but she told me about them anyway, and the little village in which she lived before coming out to Australia. They lived in a house at the end of a long lane. Their house was the last house in the lane. And from there, and this is what she told me, there were fields of wild plants. And during the warmer months, well, up would come the bluebells, and she told me about all of it. There were other plants and things as well, but I had trouble remembering all the names and all that stuff. I really liked Mrs Dean. She would bring me in little cakes. She called them Kill Stone Deads. They were a bit hard. But there was nice jam inside and sometimes there was cream, especially after pay day.

And then there was Val. She had been up north somewhere; I think it was near Alice Springs. She came into work with a lizard in a cardboard box. There was sand in the bottom of the box and the lizard looked like it would have been happier back in the desert. Val would often be seen sitting by her machine staring out the window, especially on blue sunny days. I used to reckon she was off thinking about the bush somewhere. The boss reckoned she would be a lot better off if she could find the time to watch the machine as well, if it was not too much trouble for her.

She used to talk about the outback and what it was like to be on a cattle station up north somewhere, away, out in the backblocks some-where in northern Queensland. I used to love hearing her talk about it. Sometimes, she would have her lunch at a little table near her machine. I would sit there. She would tell me about her trips and what they were like, and what it was like camping out under the stars. I could not think of a better life. She tried to explain to me that it was not all that good, not all the time. There were tough times. There were droughts, and sometimes floods which isolated people sometimes for weeks, and she told me all of it, but I still felt as if I wanted to jump on the next train heading north. I would look down through the machines and I could almost imagine as if there was sand and rocks on the factory floor but I knew it was dopey, so I tried not to think this way.

I liked Val. She wore bright clothes. She used to give a funny little whistle as she walked up and down between the machines. I could talk to Val. I think she knew of my home situation, because she lived just a few streets away. She had seen my father walking the dogs and on one occasion she had tried to start up a conversation with him, but he had just walked on. She told me he had looked straight through her.

The nights were the worst, the mealtimes the worst of all. I was a young fool. I used to bait my father. Get him going on his favourite subject. Bob Menzies, for instance. Then he would rant and rave. He would scream about working people, the unions, the Labor Party – all Commos, he would scream out. But then the silences. The stares. He would stare at each one of us in turn. My mother, me, Uncle Joe, and any of my siblings left at the table who had not left the room in fear.

I had told my mother about Val at the factory, how I liked her and how she told me all about the bush up north. My mother must have told my father about her. He screamed out. He called her a slut. He said terrible things about her. On this night, I broke down. Tears welled up inside me. I rushed out of the house and into the street, tears stream-ing down my face. I felt as if the tears were coming from deep inside my guts. I could not stop crying. I went further down the street and sat on a seat by a bus stop. I must have sat there for hours. Then I went back home and straight to my sleepout at the back. I put some music on and started to read my favourite magazine, *Wildlife*, by Crosbie Morrison. He was a naturalist, a lecturer and broadcaster. He took me into another world with his writing about the animals and the bush. Through his writings, I could feel and hear the peace of the bush.

In the distance, I could hear my father ranting. I could hear his voice screaming on the wind. I could hear my mother yelling at him and telling him not to touch any of the kids. I could hear her tell him he would feel the knife if he did. That is what she told him. I could hear it. I could hear his high-pitched screaming, his yelling about Poms and sluts and bludging workers and all of it as it came to me from the house. The yelling would subside, and then it would return, again and again. I was crying my eyes out.

I turned up the music and started to read the magazine again. I turned to the back page and noticed there were advertisements for bushwalking clubs. I thought I must do something about it sometime. I lay back on my bed. I could hear the yelling from the house. I was sure they could hear all the noise from over the road.

The moon was shining through the window onto the white wall. There were shadows from the trees outside on the wall. The wall reminded me of the screen at the Camden Theatre on a Saturday afternoon.

I started to drift off to sleep. Figures appeared on the wall as if from nowhere. I could see Val from over the road in her wheelchair. She waved to me and I waved back. I could see the nurse walking up her drive to give her the weekly injection. I could see her mother at the front door with a handkerchief clutched to her mouth. I know she was a bit far away but I was sure she had been crying. And the Camden Theatre came up and I could see Judy Garland and the *Wizard of Oz* and Hopalong Cassidy riding across the screen. And the lady from the bakery, leaning on the counter waiting for me to remember my order which I knew off by heart anyway. And Landcox Park came up and I could see the long piece of string drifting down into the water with a lump of meat on the end, and then waiting for the bite of the yabby. I could hear in the background the yelling and screaming coming from the house. I turned the music up. I found peace with the music. The music took me to other places and other people. I was away from the violence and the yelling and screaming.

The next evening, I rang the secretary of a bushwalking club. And that is a story for another day.